RAISING HEALTH...

by

Dr. Cleon V. Kimberling
and
Gerilyn Parsons

Christian Veterinary Mission

A Publication of Christian Veterinary Mission
Christian Veterinary Mission
19303 Fremont Avenue North
Seattle, WA 98133 USA
Current Book Information at:
www.cvmusa.org

PHONE: (206) 546-7569   FAX: (206) 546-7458

THIS IS THE SECOND EDITION

First published in 1998. This book can be improved with your help. If you have ideas or suggestions for ways this book could be changed in the next edition to better meet your needs, please write to us. Thank you.

Library of Congress Cataloging-in-Publication Data

Kimberling, Cleon V.
  Raising healthy sheep / by Cleon V. Kimberling and Gerilyn Parsons. -- 2nd ed.
    p. cm. -- (Raising healthy animals series)
  ISBN 978-1-886532-18-2
  1. Sheep. 2. Sheep--Diseases. 3. Sheep--Health. I. Parsons, Gerilyn. II. Christian
Veterinary Mission. III. Title. IV. Series.
  SF375.K53 2008
  636.3--dc22
                                                                    2008025426

Raising Healthy Animals Series

Every year, thousands of people around the world struggle to survive because they don't have the right knowledge, skills and resources to care for their animals. Christian Veterinary Mission (CVM) sends veterinary professionals to live and work alongside many of these people to encourage them and provide them with not only much needed veterinary expertise, but also the hope that is only found in Christ. CVM veterinarians build lasting relationships with individuals and communities, helping them be transformed through Christ's love.

CVM, in its effort to be meaningfully involved in work in the developing world, quickly found there was little appropriate educational material available. CVM set about developing basic resource materials in animal husbandry for farmers and agricultural workers. Apparently, they met a real need, as these books have been accepted throughout the developing nations of the world.

The series of books published by Christian Veterinary Mission includes the following in order of publication:

Raising Healthy Pigs *	Drugs and Their Usage
Raising Healthy Rabbits *	Where There Is No Animal Doctor
Raising Healthy Fish	Raising Healthy Horses
Raising Healthy Cattle	Zoonoses: Animal Diseases That Affect Humans
Raising Healthy Poultry *+	Raising Healthy Honey Bees
Raising Healthy Goats *	Slaughter and Preservation of Meat
Raising Healthy Sheep	Disease and Parasite Prevention in Farm Animals

[Also available in: * Spanish + French].

CVM fieldworkers have also developed specific training materials for the countries in which they work.

All of these books have been put together by Christian men and women; in a labor of love and service, for people in need throughout the world. It demonstrates dedication to their profession, service to humanity and a witness to their faith. We hope that they are a help to you in developing an appropriate livestock program to meet your needs. We pray God's blessing on their use.

Leroy Dorminy
Leroy Dorminy
CVM Founder

ACKNOWLEDGMENTS

The authors of the second edition would like to express their sincere gratitude to those individuals without whose help, talents, and patience this revision would not have been completed.

To Dr. Bill Shulaw of The Ohio State University many thanks for his wisdom and insight in the review of this book. A special word of thanks goes to Glenda T Allen for the editorial revision of the parasite section and to Jeruesha Nichols for overall editorial comments, cheerfulness and encouragement. Thanks to Dr. John Cheney of Colorado State University for the photographs in the parasite section and the many wonderful years of working together. The excellent illustrations that add so much to the text were drawn by Dennis Giddings (figures 4.1, 5.1, 6.5, and 6.7) and Lynn Kesel (5.6 and 5.7).

We would also like to thank Dr. Leroy Dorminy and Diana Baker (CVM Educational Materials Coordinator) for their assistance and patience as we struggled with locating and scanning numerous photographs presented in this publication. The photographs, with the exception of those in the parasite section, in this revision were from the photo library of Cleon Kimberling.

Thanks also to our families and friends who, as always, provide the love, support, and understanding that enabled us to undertake this labor of love.

Finally, thank you to all of those sheep producers, both at home and abroad, whose farms have served as our classrooms over the years and who themselves have been our teachers!

Dr. Mark Bounds spent the last seven years of his life in rural Bolivia, working with his wife, Dr. Susan Stewart, with whom he shared the directorship of World Concern's Latin America projects. Through their skills and dedication as veterinarians, Mark and Susan helped men and women gain the skills they needed to face the problems of poverty, illness, lack of education, and lack of resources. Mark often described their work as, "Making changes in all areas of people's lives: the spiritual, the social, the physical, and the cultural."

Mark died in Bolivia on Thursday, September 7, 1995 while serving God and his fellow man. One of Mark's requests was for a book to help farmers raise healthy sheep.

It is for this reason that "Raising Healthy Sheep" is dedicated to the late Mark Bounds in memory of his sacrifice to serve those in need through the help of God.

ABOUT THE AUTHORS

Cleon V. Kimberling is a "retired" veterinarian, after working with Colorado State University Extension for 41 years. Much of Dr. Kimberling's professional experience has been with sheep. He continues as a small ruminant consultant with his emphasis on reproductive efficiency and health. Dr. Kimberling has worked with sheep producers throughout the western United States, as well as in East Africa, the Mediterranean region, the Baltic region, Siberia and South American countries. Dr. Kimberling is an avid bicyclist and photographer.

Gerilyn Parsons is with Colorado State University Extension and the College of Veterinary Medicine and Biomedical Sciences. Geri grew up on a wheat farm in western Nebraska, USA; where her family also raised millet, sheep, cattle, pigs and chickens. Her special interests include reproductive and health management of small ruminants. She works with large range operations and small farm flocks as well as having opportunities to work with producers in the Mediterranean region and Scotland.

TABLE OF CONTENTS

Christian Veterinary Mission (Publisher of this book)

Our vision is to see

Christ's love expressed through veterinary medicine.

Our mission is to

challenge, empower and facilitate veterinarians to serve through their profession, living out their Christian faith.

CVM also provides education and encouragement for those who desire to minister through service, prayer, relationship building, and modeling Christ's love.

About CVM

Christian Veterinary Mission (CVM) is a ministry of CRISTA Ministries, a registered non-profit Christian Service Organization 501(c)(3) based in Seattle, Washington, U.S.A.

CVM was founded in 1976 by Dr. Leroy Dorminy who came to realize the impact that veterinarians could have by integrating their faith with their practice, both locally and around the world. In 2008, CVM had nearly 30 veterinary professionals serving full-time internationally and over 200 veterinary professionals and student volunteers serve on short-term cross-cultural mission trips annually. CVM sponsors fellowship & prayer breakfasts at over 20 U.S. veterinary meetings each year and reaches out to veterinary students through Christian Veterinary Fellowship (CVF) groups in every veterinary school in the U.S. by encouraging them in spiritual growth and professional development.

There are over 3,500 veterinarians affiliated with CVM in the U.S. CVM also partners with organizations and networks in other countries that are focused on empowering Christian veterinarians. CVM has a volunteer advisory board of veterinarians who guide its vision, mission, and programming.

CVM books and the free International Animal Health Newsletter were written with small farmers, veterinarians, and agricultural development workers in mind. Our desire is that they would help individuals and groups develop an appropriate livestock program to meet community needs. CVM's Endowment Fund was started in the early years of the organization's life. The fund provides for meaningful programs that could not be funded by the regular budgeting process.

Introduction:

WHY RAISE SHEEP?

Sheep are one of the most common species of livestock and were the first to be domesticated. Sheep are raised all over the world, from the deserts of Africa to the high mountains of South America. Management varies from three or four animals that live in one room of the house to groups of a thousand or more roaming the open rangelands.

There are many reasons for raising sheep. They are very adaptable and will produce milk, fiber and meat under a wide range of environmental conditions and management systems. Sheep are ideal for the smallholder wanting to provide food and fiber for the family, as well as for the commercial producer raising livestock for sale or trade. Sheep can be productive in a wide variety of climates from subtropical and temperate to semi-arid and desert. Because of their small size sheep are easily handled and often do not require special facilities.

This handbook is intended for the agricultural worker who deals with sheep producers in remote rural areas. It covers the main principles of sheep production and management with an emphasis on disease prevention. The production of high quality products from sheep is also discussed. This handbook will help the sheep producer select production goals, select the type of sheep most suitable for a particular area and will serve as a guide for the production of healthy livestock.

Section 1

Selecting Sheep That Match Available Resources

SELECTING SHEEP THAT MATCH AVAILABLE RESOURCES

Climatic conditions, feed resources, management style and desired end products (meat, milk, fiber) dictate the type of sheep best suited for each farm. Each of these factors must be considered in order to achieve optimum production.

Climatic Conditions

In many remote areas of the world sheep have adapted to the local environment over years of natural selection. Today, as the result of both natural and planned selection, there are many different breeds of sheep throughout the world. These breeds are often classified as hair sheep, fine-, medium-, or long-wooled sheep, fat tail sheep, or milk sheep. **Hair Sheep** (figure 1.1) do well in areas with high rainfall, humidity and heat. Hair sheep are efficient meat producing animals but produce a very poor quality fiber. **Fine-wool sheep** (figure 1.2) thrive in dry, temperate environments. Fine-wooled breeds can produce large quantities of garment quality wool as well as meat. They do not, however, do well under wet conditions. **Medium and course wooled sheep** (figures 1.3a & 1.3b) are kept for multiple uses and are sometimes referred to as dual purpose breeds. They produce lambs which are slaughtered for meat, they can be milked for the production of dairy products, and their wool is used for outer garments, blankets and carpets. **Fat tail sheep** (figure 1.4) are well adapted to hot desert environments. The function of the fat tail is similar to that of the hump of a camel. During times when feed is abundant, the tail serves as storage for energy which can be drawn upon later when feed is scarce. Fat tail sheep produce high quality meat, are often milked, and their coarse wool makes very durable carpets. **Milk sheep** (figure 1.5) are those breeds that have been developed to produce large quantities of milk from which cheese and yogurt are made. Breeds of sheep have been developed in areas of Europe and the Mediterranean that are noted for high milk production. The lambs from milk sheep are usually weaned at 30-45 days of age and

Shrubs are not good for sheep to eat.

are used for meat. Wool production from these sheep is minimal. Experienced sheep producers can be questioned about the local breeds in a region.

Feed Resources

The type of sheep must also be selected to match the available feed resources. Those breeds with a larger mature body size will require more feed for good production. Some breeds of sheep tend to have multiple lambs, sometimes up to four or five at a time. These breeds also require more and better quality feed than those giving birth to a single lamb. Make a list of all the possible feed sources in your locality and the time of year when these feeds are available. This will help in planning a good nutritional program which is the basis for healthy animals. Ideally, lambing time should coincide with the time when the highest quality and most abundant feed is available so that the lactating ewe will be on the highest level of nutrition. Feeds can be grazed or harvested and fed to confined sheep. Grazed feeds include grasses, shrubs, weeds and crop residues. Some areas may have forages along roads or trails that can be utilized by tethering or herding animals. Sheep will forage many plants that other livestock will not eat or that can cause harm to other livestock. Sheep can be used to manage forages, control certain plant species and help improve grazing conditions. It is important to plan ahead for supplemental feeding during periods when plant growth declines due to lack of rainfall or changes in season. Feeds that can be harvested and stored include forages, seeds and grains. The leaves and tender branches of certain trees and shrubs make excellent feed and can be harvested and fed to confined animals. See the nutrition section for a list of common forages and alternative feed that may be available for sheep production.

Management Style

The management style of the shepherd may dictate what type of sheep is raised. For example, extremely prolific breeds that have multiple lambs generally do not survive well under range conditions.

Nutrition is a big part of sheep + goats.

These breeds are better suited to a well supervised confinement operation. Small hardy sheep with strong feet and legs would be well suited to a system in which large distances are covered daily.

Desired End Products

The various breeds of sheep excel in the production of different end products. Someone interested in harvesting high quality wool would choose a different breed than someone who was primarily interested in milk production. The worker can question local sheep producers about the attributes of local breeds. The introduction of non-native breeds can also be used to select and improve chosen traits.

Figure 1.1 Hair sheep. (Katahdin male).

Figure 1.2 Fine wool sheep. (Rambouillet male).

Figure 1.3a Medium wool sheep. (Junin female).

Figure 1.3b Medium to coarse wool—meat breed. (Texel females).

Figure 1.4 Fat tail sheep. (Rahmani female).

Figure 1.5 High producing milk sheep. (Awasi females).

Section 2

Management Systems

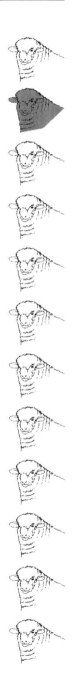

MANAGEMENT SYSTEMS

Sheep can be raised under a wide variety of management systems. Management systems are influenced by climatic conditions, feed resources and traditions. Management systems vary from extensive to intensive.

Extensive Systems

Extensive management systems (figure 2.1) include pastoral systems and range operations. With extensive systems the sheep are allowed to roam free over large areas of grazing land. These areas are usually open without fencing and the sheep are managed by a herder. Often, the land is communally managed and serves many families and multiple flocks.

Figure 2.1 Extensive management. Herder with sheep on open grazing.

Advantages
– Sheep can be moved to area where forage is available.
– Costs are minimal.
– Health problems are minimized.

Disadvantages
– Predator loss may pose a problem.
– A herder may have to stay with the sheep at all times.
– Pastures and rangeland may become over-grazed.

Intensive Systems

Intensive management systems may include intensive rotational grazing or total confinement systems. In rotational systems, the animals are confined to a relatively small area for a short period of time (24-72 hours) and then moved to another location. The previously grazed area is then allowed to regrow before being grazed again. This system utilizes moveable fencing or herders to confine the animals. In total confinement systems the sheep are kept in a pen, yard, room or may be tethered. The sheep do not graze, but are fed harvested feeds. When sheep are kept in confinement, feed and water are provided by the shepherd.

Figure 2.2 Intensive management. Small flock confinement feeding.

Advantages
- Helps prevent loss to predators.
- Nutritional intake can be regulated.
- Parasite control is simplified.

Disadvantages
- More labor is required to collect forages and feed the animals.
- Unless pens are kept clean, there can be increased disease such as pneumonia and diarrhea.

Combination Systems

Various combinations of extensive and intensive management systems can be used. In cases where there are only a small number of sheep, the sheep can be housed at night and tethered or herded during the days to utilize forage along roadsides and trails. Sheep

Figure 2.3 Intensive management. Sheep in confinement with fence line feeding. Fence line feeding helps prevent contamination of the feed.

can also be herded during periods when fresh forages are plentiful, and then penned and fed harvested feeds when fresh forages become scarce. In some parts of the world where trees and large shrubs are harvested daily for feed, the sheep are kept in confinement with protective shade.

Section 3

Selecting Healthy Breeding Stock

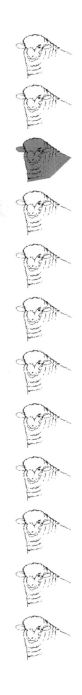

*You really want to breed your sheep well!

SELECTING HEALTHY BREEDING STOCK

The purpose of a breeding animal is reproduction. For efficient reproduction the animal must be healthy, relatively free of parasites, receiving good nutrition and have moderate body condition.

Figure 3.1 Selecting high quality, healthy breeding stock.

CHECK THE FOLLOWING:

General Attitude　　Is the animal bright and alert or dull and depressed?

Overall Appearance　Is the wool and hair bright or dull? Is the rear clean or soiled with manure?

Locomotion　　Does the animal walk freely without a limp or shortness of stride?

Eyes　　Are the eyes clear and does the animal see well?

Teeth	Are the teeth solid and do the teeth meet the dental pad?
Feet (Joint problems)	Are the hooves normal with no evidence of infection or other abnormalities?
Joints	Are the joints normal and not swollen?
Testicles (male)	Are the testicles large, the same size and free of lumps or hard swollen areas?
Prepuce (male)	Is the prepuce free of abnormalities?
Penis (male)	Does the penis have abnormal swellings or sores?
Teats (female)	Are the teats well-placed on the udder and are they normal in size?
Udder (female)	Is the udder normal size, soft and pliable without any lumps?

Sometimes they have an extra tit, and it needs to be removed b/c it doesn't give off milk.

Determining Age

The age of a sheep can be estimated by examining the front teeth of the lower jaw. A lamb has eight small temporary teeth, or milk teeth. As the animal matures, these temporary teeth are replaced by larger permanent incisor teeth. A yearling has two large central permanent incisors flanked by three pair of smaller temporary teeth (figure 3.2). A two-year-old has four large central permanent incisors with two small temporary teeth on each side (figure 3.3). The three-year-old has six large permanent incisors and a single small temporary tooth on each side (figure 3.4). Finally, the four-year-old has eight permanent incisors with no small temporary teeth remaining (figure 3.5). After four years of age, it is difficult to accurately determine the age of a sheep by looking at the teeth or by "mouthing" the sheep. In a "solid mouth" animal, all teeth are permanent, sound and firmly set. As the animal continues to age, the permanent teeth will begin to wear down, spread and loosen. Older animals are sometimes referred to as "spreaders" (figure 3.6), "broken mouths," or "gummers" based on the condition of their teeth.

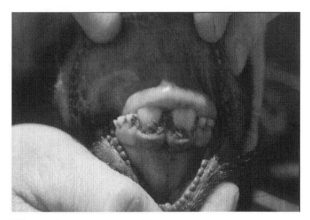

Figure 3.2 One-year-old.

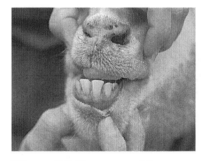

Figure 3.3 Two-year-old.

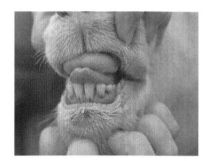

Figure 3.4 Three-year-old.

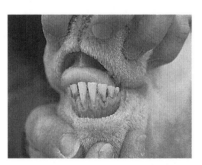

Figure 3.5 Four-year-old.

Figure 3.6 Seven-year-old.

NORMAL PHYSIOLOGICAL VALUES OF SHEEP

	Average	Range
Rectal Temperature (°C)	39.3	39.2-39.6
Heart Rate (beats/min.)	75	70-90
Respiration Rate (breaths/min.)	20	10-30

Reproductive Values:

	Average	Range
Gestation Period (days)	148	145-155
Onset of Puberty (months)	8	4-12
Estrous Cycle Length (days)	17	14-20
Length of Heat (hours)	–	24-36
Time of Ovulation	12-24 hours before the end of heat	
Optimum time to Service	18-24 hours after the onset of heat	

Sheep Milk Composition (% of fluid milk):

Water	82.9
Fat	6.2
Protein	5.4
Lactose	4.3

Daily Manure Production (kg):

Adult Sheep	2.5-8.5
Lactating Ewe	3.0
Feeder Lamb	1.8

Manure Composition (%):

Total Solids	25
Water	75

*They only live to like 12-15, and they are not at much use then.

Section 4

Sheep Nutrition

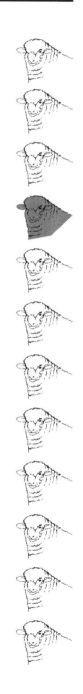

SHEEP NUTRITION

Sheep are, perhaps, the most adaptable of the domestic livestock when it comes to nutrition. They are efficient users of poor quality forages and can be productive on a wide variety of feeds. It is their ability to produce food and fiber from many different feed sources that makes sheep one of the most popular livestock species world-wide.

Ruminant Digestion

Ruminants, including sheep, goats, cattle and buffalo get their name from the largest compartment of their gastrointestinal (GI) tract, the rumen (figure 4.1). The rumen serves as a storage compartment and contains microorganisms, including bacteria and protozoa that are able to digest high fiber food. When a sheep eats, it chews its food slightly then swallows and passes it into the rumen where strong contractions mix the food with water. Reverse contractions of the esophagus then bring this feed mixed with water back up into the sheep's mouth, where it can be chewed again to assist in further digestion. This is called "chewing the cud."

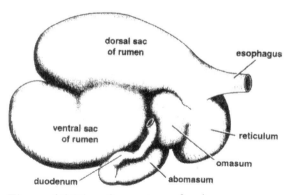

Figure 4.1 Digestive system of a sheep.

The feed is again swallowed and rumen microorganisms digest the fiber and release products that the sheep can absorb for energy. Fermentation gasses such as methane are also produced and are eructated, or burped up, by the sheep. The microorganisms themselves eventually flow out of the rumen through the GI tract, where

*If an animal is getting the right amount of nutrition they won't graze all day, but if they aren't then they will graze all day.

they are digested and provide important nutrients such as protein and vitamins. Actually, ruminant nutrition involves feeding the rumen microorganisms which in turn will feed the animal.

Essential Nutrients

Water (Water needs to be clean!)

No living creature can survive without water. Ruminants have a high requirement for water due to the fermentation process that occurs in the rumen. Estimated daily water requirements for sheep are:

4 liters (1 gal.) for ewes on dry feed
6 liters (1.5 gal.) for ewes nursing lambs
2 liters (0.5 gal.) for growing lambs

If water is limited, feed consumption will decrease and production will be low. During warm weather it is best to water sheep at least once per day. Where distances between watering sites are great or where water must be hauled in, sheep may be watered every other day. Sheep will eat snow and do not need additional water if the snow is soft. If it is crusted over with ice, the surface must be broken to allow sheep access to the snow underneath.

Figure 4.2 Water is an essential nutrient.

The most important time for an animal to get nutrition is when they are pregnant + after they give birth.

Energy

In most sheep producing areas of the world energy is the nutrient that is most likely to be limited in the diet. Inadequate energy results in poor growth, reduced reproductive ability and increased susceptibility to disease. Energy requirements depend on the size of the animal, its growth or reproductive stage and on environmental factors like weather, availability of shelter and the terrain. All animals require high quality feed; larger animals require more feed intake. Breeds with large mature frame size and heavy mature body weight have a higher energy requirement than do the smaller breeds. Ewes have the highest requirement for energy during the last month of pregnancy and the first month of milk production.

Growing lambs also have a high energy requirement which is usually met by milk consumption for the first 6-8 weeks of life. After this period, lambs begin to consume significant amounts of solid feed and grow rapidly until approximately 8 months of age. Sheep usually reach their mature body size sometime during their second year of life. Pen-fed or tethered sheep have lower energy requirements than do range or pastured sheep. Grazing over large areas of steep, rough terrain can increase energy requirements by as much as ten times. Cold, wet or windy weather also increases energy requirements. Because of the many factors that affect the amount of energy a sheep requires, it is important to examine animals frequently to be sure that their needs are being met. Feel the tissue cover over the ribs, spine and hips to estimate body condition (figure 4.3).

Figure 4.3 Palpating the fat covering of the spine and lateral processes.

The appearance of wooled sheep can be deceiving. Only by feeling under the wool can the condition of the animal be determined.

High energy feeds include grains, root crops, legumes and the early vegetative stages of grasses. Estimates of daily energy requirements can be found in **Table 1.0.**

Protein

Protein is necessary for building body tissues such as muscle, skin, hooves and wool. Ruminants get most of their protein by digesting the microorganisms that pass out of their rumen. Therefore, if the rumen contains a healthy population of microorganisms, the sheep will get enough protein. These organisms themselves have a requirement for either protein or nitrogen in order to grow and reproduce. Many native grasses and grains fed to sheep provide adequate protein for most situations. The exceptions to this would be young growing lambs or ewes producing large quantities of milk. Diets of straw (the stem of small grains), corn stalks or dried mature grasses need to be supplemented with protein for all livestock groups (figure 4.4). Good sources of protein include legume forages, some leguminous and nonleguminous trees and shrubs, peas and beans, oil meals, meat and blood meals, feather meal, dairy byproducts and fish meal.

Figure 4.4 Corn stalks and stover make excellent forage, but may need to be supplemented with protein.

Figure 4.5 The leaves and tender branches of some trees and shrubs make excellent feed for sheep.

Estimates of the protein needs of sheep can be found in **Table 1.0**.

Table 1.0   Nutritional Requirements of Sheep

Stage of Production	Digestible Energy (Meal)	Crude Protein (gm)	Dry Matter Intake (% body wt)
Maintenance (60 kg ewe)	2.7	104	2
Last month of pregnancy	4.4	184	3
1st month of milk production	6.6	319	4
2-3 month old weaned lamb (10 kg)	1.8	127	5
3-6 month old weaned lamb (30 kg)	4.4	191	4
6-12 month old lamb (40kg)	5.4	185	4

Since the rumen microorganisms can use nitrogen to make protein, it is possible to use non-protein nitrogen (NPN) in ruminant diets. The chemical urea and ammonia-treated straw are the most commonly used forms of NPN. **Although NPN use can be an inexpensive way to add protein to a diet, NPN can be poisonous if used improperly or fed to very young animals.** Therefore, the addition of NPN to ruminant rations should only be done by persons trained in its use.

Vitamins
Under normal conditions the rumen microorganisms produce adequate amounts of the **B vitamins** to meet the needs of the sheep. Sheep can also produce their own **vitamin C**. The vitamins that must be provided in the diet are **vitamins A, D and E**. Green pasture forages and green leafy feeds are good sources of vitamins A and E. Sheep can store enough vitamin A in the liver to last them for 6-12 weeks. Vitamin E is also present in grain seeds. Vitamin D is manufactured in the body when the sheep are exposed to strong sunlight. Deficiencies can occur in animals that are confined indoors, but sheep on pasture rarely need additional vitamin D.

Minerals
Minerals play a vital role in many body functions and help build strong healthy bodies. **Calcium** helps build strong bones. **Phos-**

2 parts Calcium, 1 part phosphorus.

phorus is important in bone formation and reproduction. **Selenium** helps build strong muscles. **Magnesium** is important in the heart functions and nervous system. Many minerals and vitamins work together. **Selenium** and **vitamin** E work together to prevent white muscle disease, also known as stiff lamb disease, a deficiency that causes weakness and death in lambs. A combination of **calcium**, **phosphorus** and **vitamin D** are all necessary for normal bone formation. **Salt** has many regulatory functions in the body. When deprived of salt, feed and water intake is decreased, and milk production and growth rate are reduced. **Sulfur** is important for wool growth, a good appetite and weight gain. **Cobalt** promotes the production of **vitamin B12** in the rumen which influences the appetite, the estrous cycle, milk production, wool growth and growth in general. **Copper** deficiencies can cause swayback in lambs and lead to weakness so the lambs are unable to nurse and die of starvation. In older sheep, copper deficiency causes abnormal wool growth, commonly known as "steely wool." Sheep do not tolerate excess copper, and copper poisoning will cause rupture of the red blood cells, anemia and death. **Iodine** deficiency will cause goiter or "big neck" in newborn lambs. **Manganese** is important to growth, reproduction and skeletal formation. **Zinc** is important for the appetite, wool and growth. Zinc helps build a good immune system. Zinc also has an important function in reproduction, male testicular development and sperm production. In the female, zinc affects all phases of the reproductive cycle.

Mineral deficiencies occur in regions where the soil is lacking in certain nutrients. This affects the concentration of these elements in the plants eaten by the sheep. Some minerals can also be poisonous if present in higher than normal amounts. Since these problems depend on the specific conditions in each sheep production region, specialists who are familiar with the area should be contacted concerning the need for mineral supplementation in the sheep diet. In many regions of the world, minerals are mixed with salt and supplied free choice to the sheep in a granular or block form.

Need alot of raw roughage (over 50%)

Roughage
Ruminants require a minimum amount of roughage in their diet to prevent digestive problems. Feeding a ration that is too high in

concentrates (high energy or protein feeds) like grain will result in illness and sometimes death. A good rule of thumb is to limit the feeding of grains and other supplements to less than 50% of the total dry matter content of the diet.

Developing a Ration for Sheep

In order to balance a ration for sheep, it is necessary to determine what feeds are available. In semi-arid climates, this usually includes native forages and limited amounts of grains like wheat or barley. Irrigated regions may have crop residues, grain and cultivated forages like alfalfa, berseem, maize or sorghum. Sheep fed near urban centers may also consume human food wastes including fruits, vegetables and bread. Reference values for the nutritional analysis of many of these feeds are available. Ideally, each source of food should be analyzed to determine its energy value, protein percentage and vitamin and mineral concentrations. Practically, however, this is often not possible due to the unavailability or prohibitive cost of analytical laboratories. In the case of native forages, trees and shrubs, these analyses may not be available. It is helpful in these situations to question successful sheep producers about their feeding practices in order to pass this information along to those who may be less knowledgeable. When forage and feed analysis is unknown, it is necessary to do periodic **B**ody **C**ondition **S**coring (see section on BCS) to determine if the nutrient requirements of the sheep are being met.

Figure 4.6 Balancing a ration.

Common Forages

- *Native Grasses, Shrubs and Weeds*
  These plants can be grazed or harvested. The harvested plants can be fed fresh daily or cured and stored to be fed during the non-growing season.

- *Cultivated Grasses and Forages*
  A wide range of grasses can be planted either in cultivated fields or interseeded into nontillable areas to improve native ranges. There are many annual grasses that are adapted to various climates that can be planted and either grazed or harvested.

- *Leguminous and Nonleguminous Trees and Shrubs*
  The leaves and tender branches of some trees and shrubs make excellent feed for sheep. Some have high quality protein and energy.

Alternative Feed Sources

- *Crop Residues*
  The straw from cereal grains, peas, teff, beans and other crops make excellent forage for feeding during periods when plant growth is dormant. Tops of many plants such as turnips, beets and carrots also make excellent feed. These can be fed in the fresh state or dried and used later. Sheep do an excellent job of cleaning fields following harvest to pick up the fallen seeds and plant residues. Sheep can also eat coarse roughage such as corn stover, which is left following harvest of the grain.

- *Tubers or Root Crops*
  There are a variety of root crops that are adaptable to most all climatic conditions of the tropic, semitropical or temperate

Figure 4.7 Potatoes and other root crops make excellent feed.

zones of the world. Most of these are grown for human consumption. Any of these can also be used for sheep feed. The waste or byproducts of these plants make excellent sheep feed. Examples include potatoes, onions, yams, turnips and parsnips (figure 4.7).

• *Food Processing Byproducts*
Many byproducts from food, grain and oil seeds make good sheep feed. These include such products as brewers grain, soybean oil meal, sunflower oil meal, rapeseed oil meal, almond waste, dates, olives, figs, coconut pulp, citrus pulp, pineapple pulp, bakery waste and other byproducts from fruit or vegetable processing. Most any byproduct from food processing can be utilized as sheep feed and will vary in its nutritional value depending on its composition.

An estimate of the nutritional value of some feeds used for sheep can be found in **Table 2.0**.

Table 2.0   Estimated Nutritional Content of Selected Feeds, As Fed

	% Dry Matter	Digestible Energy (Mcal/kg)	% Crude % Protein (As Fed)
Fresh Forages			
Grasses	26	0.76	4.9
Desert Browse	23	0.52	4.0
Alfalfa (lucerne)	24	0.62	4.8
Clover	26	0.80	4.0
Small grain pasture (wheat, barley, oats, rye)	22	0.73	6.3
Hay			
Alfalfa (lucerne)	90	2.2	16.2
Grass	91	2.2	8.8
Straw (wheat, oat, barley)	89	1.6	3.2
Grains			
Maize (corn)	88	3.4	8.9
Oats	89	3.0	11.8
Barley	88	3.4	11.9
Wheat	89	3.4	14.2
Rice (polished)	89	3.6	7.2
Food by-products			
Citrus fruit pulp (dried)	91	3.4	6.1
Olive waste (dried)	92	?	6.4
Rice bran (not hulls)	91	3.0	12.7
Wheat bran	89	2.8	11.8
Almond hulls	90	2.2	2.0
Dried beans	89	3.7	25.3
Fish meal (dried)	92	2.8	61.1
Turnips	9	0.35	0.8

Calculating a Ration

As an example, we will calculate a ration for a 60 kg ewe in late pregnancy using barley, wheat straw and grass hay. Balance first for energy content.

*A prego sheep needs at least 60% protein.

— 43 —

Babies need a high nutrition!

This ewe's energy requirement is 4.4 Mcal per day. She can consume 3% of her body weight in dry matter.

60 kg x 3% = 1.8 kg of dry matter per day

Since straw is the cheapest feed available, we will determine how much energy is contained in 1.8 kg of straw dry matter.

1.8 kg/89% dry matter = 2.0 kg
2.0 kg x 1.6 Mcal/kg = 3.2 Mcal energy

It is obvious that the ewe cannot consume enough straw to meet her energy needs. Therefore, the next calculation will determine the energy content in 1.8 kg of hay dry matter.

1.8 kg/91% dry matter = 2.0 kg
2.0 kg x 2.2 Mcal/kg = 4.4 Mcal energy

This amount of hay contains adequate energy to meet the ewe's needs.

Next, determine the protein contained in the hay.

2.0 kg x 8.8% protein = 176 gm protein

The ewe's requirement is 184 gm. Therefore, there is a deficit of 184 – 176 = 8 gm.

Since the barley has the highest protein content, determine how much barley must be fed to gain 8 gm of protein.

8 gm x 100 gm barley / 11.9 gm protein = 67 gm barley

This amount of barley provides 0.06 kg dry matter which is negligible. This results in a ration comprised of:

Ingredient	Dry Matter (kg)	Mcal	Protein (gm)
2.0 kg grass hay	1.8	4.4	176
70 gm barley	–	0.2	8
Total	1.8	4.6	184

In most cases, the feed is not weighed exactly, but the amount is estimated. However, some standard of measure that is fairly reliable should be used. Adjustments to the ration should be made if the animals become too thin or too heavy.

Feeding During the Production Year

Breeding (0-14 days)
Increasing the energy content of the ratio for a two week period before and during breeding (called "flushing") can result in an increased number of ovulations and lead to more lambs being born. Examples include adding 0.25 kg grain/ewe/day, or changing to higher quality forage such as alfalfa hay or hay field aftermath, forage brassica (turnips, rape, kale) or fresh pasture. In some parts of the world, clover (especially subterranean clover) has high estrogen content and can reduce fertility. Discuss this with local agriculturists to determine if the problem is present in your region. If it is, then clover should be avoided during the breeding period. In order to enhance the survivability of the fertilized ovum, the increased energy level should be maintained for at least two weeks following breeding.

Early Pregnancy (14-50 days)
Feed the ewe to maintain her body condition. Examples include grazing winter range or stockpiled winter pasture, or providing moderate quality grass hay (10-12% protein).

Mid-Pregnancy (50-100 days)
Feed to maintain a good body condition. Check ewes for condition every 2-3 weeks and adjust the ration accordingly. This is the period of placental development, and the ewe will absorb multiple fetuses, leaving only one, if nutritionally stressed. Acceptable rations are basically the same as those used during early pregnancy but may need to be supplemented depending on weather and forage conditions.

Late Pregnancy (100-148 days)

This period requires an increasing energy content in the feed because seventy-five percent of fetal growth occurs during the last six weeks of pregnancy. In addition, twin-bearing ewes need almost twice as much energy as single-bearing ewes, and triplet-bearing ewes need 2.5 times more energy. Examples for a 60 kg ewe are 1.5 kg good quality hay (12-14% protein) + 0.5 kg grain, or good fresh pasture + 0.25-0.5 kg grain. If the flock has a history of ewes producing two or three lambs, then the energy should be increased by 50-100%. **Straw is not an adequate ration for ewes in late pregnancy.** Again, it is wise to get advice from successful and respected sheep producers in the region about the best way to use the feeds that are available.

Lactation (Milking)

This is the period of greatest energy requirement. Ideally, it will occur during the period of fastest pasture growth. Ewes nursing more than two lambs require additional protein beyond that present in native forages. Expect a moderate loss of body condition during lactation. Peak milk production occurs three to four weeks after lambing so supplementation can be tapered off after that. Examples of adequate rations include lush spring pasture, or 2 kg grass/legume hay + 1.0 kg grain. **A straw diet will not meet the needs of lactating ewes, even with grain supplementation.**

Dry Period

The dry period occurs between weaning of the lambs and the next breeding season. This is the time when the ewes regain body condition lost during lactation. Their requirements are not high during the dry period and can be met by grazing or eating medium quality forage.

Lamb Creep Feed

A "creep feeder" is a feed area where lambs can have free access to high quality feeds other than their mother's milk and older sheep are excluded. This allows the lambs to eat a specific high quality ration which older sheep do not need. It is especially useful in situations where lambs will be weaned at 8-12 weeks of age since the lambs learn to eat solid feed before the stress of weaning takes place. Creep feeding is also beneficial in situations where animals of all ages are housed in one group since it allows extra supplementation of young growing lambs. A hole or slot in a fence allows access to the creep areas by the lambs and keeps the adult animals out. The area should be clean, dry and well-lighted to attract the lambs. Lambs will begin eating coarsely ground grains or leafy legume hay at 10-14 days of age. In some cases, a reverse creep may be used when lower quality harvested forages are being fed to the adults and the lambs are allowed to graze on high quality fresh forages.

Weaned Lambs

Growing lambs have much higher nutritional requirements than do adult ewes. After weaning, lambs can be fed in confinement or grazed ahead of ewes in an intensive grazing system. Under some management system, lambs are left with the ewes until they are sold or slaughtered. However, during times of the year when grazing is limited, it is usually more efficient to separate the lambs at two to four months of age and feed them high quality feeds like grain or cultivated crops. This will allow the ewes to maintain themselves on available native forages.

Body Condition Scoring

Body Condition Scoring (**BCS**) is a tool that the producer can use to determine whether the nutritional requirements of the animal are being provided. The universal body condition scoring system is based on a scale from one to five—with one being extremely thin and three being extremely fat. For simplicity, one could use a three point system with one being "too thin," two being in moderate condition, and five being "too fat." To determine the body condition, one must feel the covering over the backbone, ribs and transverse processes of the vertebrae. It is essential that one place his/her hands directly on these areas and feel the flesh covering, as even a short wool coat can make a thin animal appear to be in moderate or good condition.

Animals that are "too thin:"

1. Have a poorer chance of breeding (conceiving).
2. Are more prone to disease because the immune system does not function as well.
3. Produce less colostrums of lower quality and thus do not pass adequate protection to the newborn lambs.
4. Produce less milk and wool.
5. Have decreased mothering instincts.
6. Are prone to metabolic disease like "twin lamb paralysis."
7. Produce weak, unthrifty lambs.

Animals that are "too fat:"

1. Have difficulty breeding (conceiving).
2. Have difficulty in lambing.
3. Have poor colostrums and milk production.
4. Are prone to metabolic diseases.
5. Have poor mothering instincts.

The good producer will examine the sheep on a routine basis to determine if the nutritional level is appropriate. Some sheep with chronic disease or parasites will not respond to improved nutrition. The problem should be diagnosed and treated accordingly. The "fat ewe" may be an aggressive member of the flock. It may require separation of this ewe from the others to limit her feed intake.

NOTE!
Accurate Body Condition Scoring is done by feeling the covering over the backbones, ribs, and transverse processes of the vertebrae.

The "thin ewe" will have:

1. The backbone protruding with the muscles along the spine wasted away.
2. The flesh and muscles over the rump wasted away with the hip and pelvic bones protruding.
3. The ribs distinct and protruding.
4. The area around the ribs and under the transverse processes of the vertebrae sunken.

The "moderate or good" conditioned ewe will have:

1. Good muscle covering over the back and rump.
2. Good covering over the ribs and transverse processes of the vertebrae.
3. The abdominal wall behind the ribs and under the transverse processes filled in.

The "too fat" ewe will have rolls of fat over the rump, back and brisket.

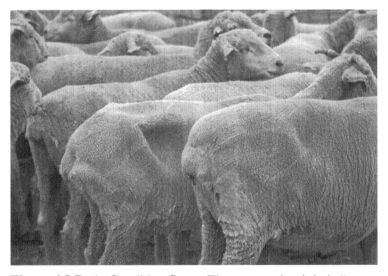

Figure 4.8 Body Condition Score. The ewe on the right is "too fat," the ewe on the left is "too thin."

Economic Considerations

Maximum production, such as high growth rates in lambs, is not always an economically sound goal. This is especially true in regions where farmers do not have cash to use for the purchase of feeds. It is very important to attempt to calculate the cost per unit of production before recommending a particular feeding program. For example, when considering rations for growing lambs, the cost per pound of gain should be determined. In order to be able to make these estimations, it may be necessary to set up feeding trials that compare two different feeding methods. These trials can be done on local farms with the cooperation of the sheep producers. On-farm trials can serve as valuable demonstrations for local producers and supply the agricultural worker with additional information on which to base recommendations.

Section **5**

Reproduction

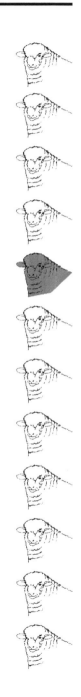

REPRODUCTION

Sexual Activity

Sexual activity in sheep is regulated by the amount of daylight. In temperate climates, the shortening of the daylight hours sends a signal to the brain to produce melatonin, a substance which activates the hormones that stimulate sexual activity in sheep. When the daylight hours begin to lengthen, the process is reversed and sexual activity in sheep begins to decline. In some geographic areas, sexual activity may become completely dormant during extended periods of daylight. In other geographic locations, sexual activity may be continuous year around, particularly as you approach the equator where there are little fluctuations in daylight hours. There are also breed variations in sexual activity. Some breeds of sheep, such as the Dorset, have continuous sexual activity even in temperate zones where daylight fluctuates with the seasons.

Flock Improvement

One method that can be used to improve the quality of local sheep, which are already adapted to the environment, is to import outside genetics. First determine which characteristics of the native sheep you want to improve and then select a breeding ram that is superior in these traits from an outside source. A slower, but still effective, method of improving the quality of local sheep is by selective breeding within the flock. Determine which animals have the desired characteristics and select offspring from these animals for replacements. Characteristics such as wool production, milk production, twinning and meat production must be measured and recorded. This will allow for accurate selection of the desired breeding animals.

Definitions of Reproductive Terms

Estrus   The episodic, restricted period of sexual receptivity in female mammals, marked by intense sexual urge. The ESTRUS

PERIOD lasts for an average of 29 hours in the ewe.

Estrous Cycle   The cycle of changes in the genital tract which is produced as a result of hormonal activity. The estrous cycle indicates the length of time between estrus periods and averages nearly 17 days in the ewe.

Ovary   The sex gland in the female that produces the ovum or egg.

Ovarian Follicle   The cells in the ovary that produce hormones which control estrus and produce the egg or ovum. When the follicle matures, it ruptures releasing an egg or ovum into the oviduct which is connected to the uterus. The rupture of the follicle occurs late in the ESTRUS PERIOD. The released egg or ovum lives about 5-8 hours if not fertilized.

Corpus Luteum   The corpus luteum, also called the "yellow body," is formed where the follicle ruptures. It produces the hormone progesterone which is responsible for maintaining pregnancy. If pregnancy does not occur, the corpus luteum shrinks, a new follicle starts to develop, and the cycle is repeated in about 17 days.

Fertilization   Fertilization occurs when the sperm from the ram unites with the ovum (egg). This usually occurs as the ovum moves down the oviduct from the ovary to the horn of the uterus and meets the sperm as it swims up the oviduct.

Zygote	The cell that results from the fertilized ovum (egg). This cell starts dividing and floats around in the uterus until it becomes attached to uterine wall. This takes from 10-14 days. This period is very critical. Stress and poor nutrition may prevent this attachment or result in a poor attachment which can result in small, weak lambs.
Nidation	Nidation is the attachment of the new embryo to the uterine wall.
Embryo	The embryo is the early developmental stage of the fertilized ovum after its attachment to the uterine wall.
Fetus	The developing embryo becomes a fetus as cell division progresses and the differentiation of body parts is completed. This occurs somewhere around 20-28 days.
Placenta	The placenta is the tissues that cover the developing fetus and attach it to the mother via the cotyledons and umbilical cord.
Gestation	Gestation is the period of pregnancy. It begins at the time of fertilization and lasts for about 148 days. Gestation length can vary between ewes.
Parturition	Parturition is the delivery of the fully developed fetus.
Abortion	The premature expulsion of the fetus from the uterus.
Stillbirth	The birth of a fully developed dead fetus.

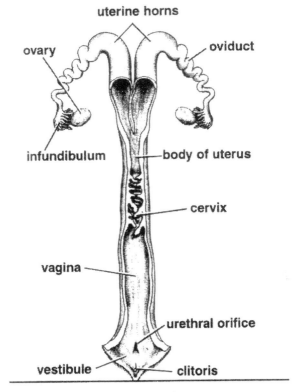

Figure 5.1 Female reproductive tract.

Breeding Season Management

Selection

Sexually mature animals with desirable traits should be the only ones selected for the breeding program. The age when female lambs reach sexual maturity will vary with the nutritional plane and growth of the animal. In general, female lambs will become sexually mature and capable of breeding at 6-8 months of age. Selecting offspring from early sexually maturing parents will improve the chances that those offspring will also mature early. Selecting animals with desirable characteristics is extremely important as both good and bad traits are passed on to the offspring. The ram is responsible for the majority of changes in the flock so select for good traits and not bad ones.

Preparing the Female

After selecting ewes for breeding, body condition is the next most important factor to be considered in the breeding program. For best results, the ewes should be in moderate body condition. In a moderately conditioned ewe, the ribs, spine and hips can be felt but are not sharply protruding. Two weeks before breeding the plane of nutrition should be increased so there is an increase in body condition. This is known as "flushing." Flushing increases the number of eggs released at the time of ovulation and, providing the nutrition is adequate and stress is minimal, increases the opportunity for twins and triplets. If internal parasites are a problem, deworming should also be a part of the "flushing" program. Heavily wooled ewes may need to have the wool around the vulva clipped to facilitate in the breeding process.

Preparing the Male

A complete breeding soundness examination should be part of the selection criteria for the ram. The ram should undergo a complete physical exam for structural and reproductive soundness. This examination should include the feet, legs, teeth, eyes, testicles and prepuce, as well as general overall appearance.

Figure 5.2 Ram breeding soundness examinations.

The ram should be bright and alert and free from any signs of illness. The prepuce should be smooth and free from any scabs or sores. The testicles should be large and firm without any abnormal lumps or defects. Palpable lumps may indicate a disease process that could compromise the fertility of the ram.

When possible, a semen sample should also be collected and examined microscopically before the ram is turned in with the ewes. Nutrition should be good so the ram has a moderate body condition. A ram in good physical condition with large testicles can serve 50-75 ewes in a 17 day cycle.

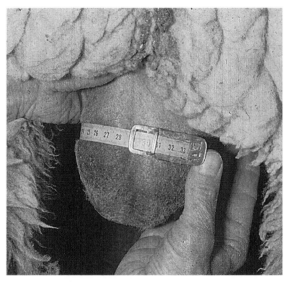

Figure 5.3 Rams with larger scrotal circumference have greater breeding capacity and produce more twins.

Breeding Period

The length of the breeding period may vary with each flock depending on the management. It is helpful to identify or know the ewes and record the breeding date. If the breeding date is recorded, then you can be prepared for and anticipate when the ewe will lamb. This will help in preventing the death of the newborn lamb if it needs assistance. If a marking harness or colored fluid is placed

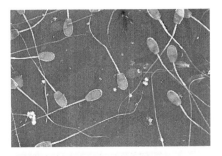

Figure 5.4 High quality semen sample. Normal sperms cells.

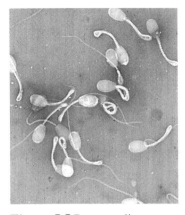

Figure 5.5 Poor quality semen sample. Note the sperm cell abnormalities.

on the ram's chest, a mark will appear on the back of ewes that are bred and breeding dates can be recorded. In some flocks, the males are left with the flock all year round. In this management system, it is helpful to feel the udders of the ewes every 2-3 weeks and remove ewes that are close to lambing so they can receive special care.

Gestation Period
The normal gestation period (time from breeding until parturition) averages about 148 days, but there is wide variability between animals and breeds. The fetus grows slowly for the first 90-100 days. The majority (75%) of fetal growth occurs during the last 50 days of gestation.

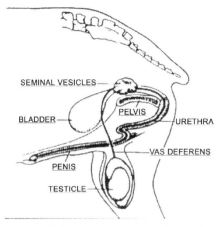

Figure 5.6 Cross section of the male reproductive tract.

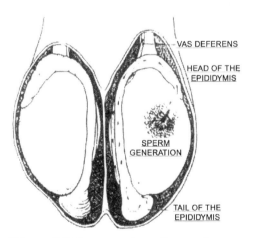

Figure 5.7 Cross section of normal testes.

Section 6

Lambing Management

LAMBING MANAGEMENT

Shearing

If shelter from inclement weather is available, heavily wooled ewes should be shorn 4-6 weeks prior to lambing. This makes it easier for the lamb to find the teat and improves sanitation. In addition, a shorn ewe is more likely to seek out shelter when she lambs rather than exposing the lamb to cold, wet conditions. If shearing is not possible, the wool should be trimmed away from the udder so that the lamb does not suck on dirty wool tags instead of the teat.

Location

Place the ewe in a familiar and comfortable environment. A strange place will cause stress and complications with mis-mothering and other problems at lambing time. The area should be clean, dry, protected from the weather and free from distractions such

Figure 6.1 Shorn ewes with clean udders reduce disease in the lambs.

Figure 6.2 Unshorn mother. Note the unsanitary condition of the wool.

Figure 6.3 Unshorn mother. Note the clean wool condition.

as dogs. During warm, dry weather, ewes can lamb out on clean pastures or on the range if predators are not a threat.

Equipment and Supplies
Iodine or another disinfectant to apply to the naval will reduce the chances of infection. A bottle with nipple or a feeding tube will

help in cases where the lamb is weak and unable to nurse. Soap, water and disinfectant should be available to clean the shepherd's hands and the ewe in case assistance with delivery is necessary. Plastic obstetrical gloves/sleeves are helpful in preventing infection to the person assisting the ewe from any infections the ewe may have.

Delivery

A few hours before delivery, the ewe will become uneasy or appear nervous. She will separate herself from the other sheep and seek a place to have her lamb. At this point in time, the vulva is very relaxed and the udder enlarged and full. The membranes or water sac will appear in the vagina and protrude from the vulva. When the water sac breaks, the ewe will usually go into labor within an hour. The ewe will usually lie down and start straining with contractions of the uterus. In a normal delivery, the front feet are presented into the birth canal first. The muzzle and head will be presented next with the head lying between the legs. If there are twins, the second lamb will usually be born within 30 minutes after the first. To determine if a second lamb is present, push your fist up into the right flank and try to bump the fetus. If there is a

Figure 6.4 Normal delivery.

second lamb, it will be easily bumped. A normal delivery, from the time the feet appear, will only take a few minutes. Ewes delivering their first lamb will take more time. If the ewe is strong and healthy, she will immediately get up and clean her lamb. The lamb will be up and try to nurse within 30 minutes.

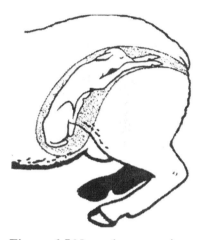

Figure 6.5 Normal presentation.

DO NOT INTERFERE UNLESS THERE IS SOME DEVIATION FROM THE ABOVE ROUTINE.

When to Assist

If the ewe appears nervous and uneasy, getting up and down for more than 2 hours without any signs of membranes or labor, she should be checked.

If the water has broken and the ewe does not start labor or straining within 1-2 hours, she should be checked.

If the ewe is in labor and straining for more than 30 minutes without any signs of fetal parts, she should be checked.

If fetal parts appear and the lamb is not delivered within about 10 minutes, the ewe should be assisted.

Assisting the Birth

Have an assistant restrain or hold the ewe. With warm water and soap thoroughly clean the vaginal area of the ewe and then clean your arms and hands. Wearing plastic sleeves with lubricant gently enter the vagina. When sleeves are unavailable utilize soap and water on your hand and arm for lubrication. IF the cervix is dilated, proceed to examine and determine the position of the lamb or lambs. Grasp the two front feet and gently pull them into the birth canal. It may be necessary to hold the front feet with the opposite hand while you direct the muzzle into the birth canal. BE GENTLE. Pull when the ewe strains. When she relaxes, do not pull.

If the feet appear and nothing else, you should determine if they belong to the front end of the lamb or to the back end.

If they are front feet, the pads will be down.

If they are back feet, the pads will be pointed up, and you can feel the hock joint on the hind leg.

If the back legs are presented (posterior presentation), grasp them in one hand and apply a gentle pull. Use the other hand to gently work the vulva over the hips. Once the hips have passed, the lamb should be delivered without delay as the umbilical cord has been pinched off.

If the tail is the only part presented (breech presentation), you will need to push the lamb ahead, cup the back feet in the palm of your hand and bring them into the birth canal. The delivery is then the same as described for a posterior presentation.

If the front feet appear but no muzzle, the head is turned back. You must push the lamb back while straightening the head and directing it into the birth canal. With one hand, pull on the legs while using the other hand to work the vagina over the head. Once the head and shoulders have passed, the lamb delivers immediately.

If the head appears and no feet (shoulder lock), the lamb must be pushed back until the front feet can be brought into the birth canal.

With the feet and muzzle in the birth canal, apply a gentle pull and deliver as directed above.

If the head and one front foot appears or the head is farther out of the birth canal than the feet (elbow lock), the lamb must be pushed back. Grasp the upper part of the leg in your hand; push back on the shoulder and at the same time forward on the elbow. With both legs straightened, pull them into the birth canal and deliver as directed above. In the case of twins, one must determine which legs belong to which lamb before a delivery can be made.

Figure 6.6 Difficult lambing. Ewe is too thin. This ewe will have poor colostrums and poor milk production.

Figure 6.6A Difficult lambing. Hip lock.

Abnormal Presentations

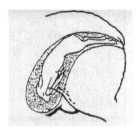

Figure 6.7a Posterior presentation.

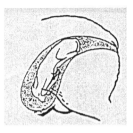

Figure 6.7b Breech.

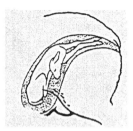

Figure 6.7c Head back.

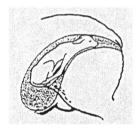

Figure 6.7d Shoulder lock.

Figure 6.7e Elbow lock.

Figure 6.7f One leg back.

Care of the Newborn

Upon delivery, most newborn lambs will shake their head, sneeze and sputter to clear the mucous. In a short time, the ewe will rise and immediately start cleaning the mucous and membranes from the lamb. By the time this process is completed, the lamb will struggle to its feet and start seeking a teat. It is important to have the wool removed from the ewe, especially around the udder, so the lamb can find the teats.

Section 7

Production Procedures

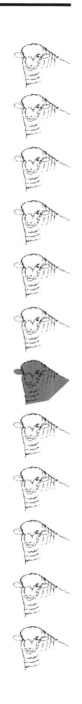

PRODUCTION PROCEDURES

The Newborn Lamb

Clip the Naval
With a clean scissors, cut the umbilical cord leaving a stump of about 1-1½ cm.

Dip the Naval
Dip the naval in an iodine solution. A strong tincture of iodine or tamed iodine can be used. If iodine is not available, dilute bleach (1:40 with water) can be used. A 1% chlorhexidine acetate (Novalsan) solution works well if the product is available.

Strip
Strip some milk from each teat to remove the waxy plug. Check the milk for any abnormalities.

Observe
Observe the lamb to make certain it is able to stand and nurse. If the lamb cries, it is probably hungry. Pick the lamb up and feel the stomach. You should be able to feel a stomach full of milk.

Nurse
If the lamb is weak and is unable to nurse within the first 30-60 minutes, help should be provided. Lay the ewe on her side and lay the lamb down so that it can nurse the bottom teat. The lamb may need assistance by placing the teat in its mouth and milking a small amount of milk into the mouth.

Figure 7.1 Signs of starvation; weak, gaunt, hunched up stance.

To ensure a strong healthy lamb, it is critical that the lamb receives a quantity of colostrum equal to about five percent of its

Figure 7.2 Assisting the lamb to nurse by laying the ewe on her side. Nurse the bottom teat.

body weight during the first 10 to 12 hours of life. Colostrum is the first milk of the ewe and contains antibodies important for lamb survival. As a general rule, the lamb should receive 25 mls of colostrum per kg body weight immediately, and repeat every 2-4 hours.

Tube Feeding
If the lamb is unable to suckle, feed by placing a tube into the stomach. Hold the lamb on your lap. Lay the feeding tube along the side of the lamb with the tip on the last rib. Measure to the mouth and put a mark on the tube. This will tell you how far to insert the tube so that the end is in the stomach. With one hand, hold the head. With the other hand, insert the feeding tube down the esophagus. Observe the skin along the left side of the neck. You can see the tube as it is passed down the esophagus. If you do not see the tube and the lamb coughs, the tube is probably in the trachea (windpipe). Remove the tube and start again.

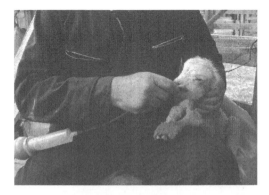

Figure 7.3a Place the tube in the lamb's mouth and gently pass it down the esophagus. Feel the tube pass under your fingers along the left side of the neck.

Figure 7.3b Gently give 25 mls colostrum per kg body weight.

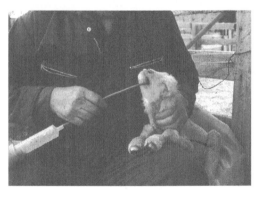

Figure 7.3c Pinch the tube when removing to prevent colostrum from draining into the trachea (windpipe).

Birth to Two Weeks of Age

Castration

Castrate the male lambs at an early age (before 2 weeks) to reduce the shock. Restrain the lamb by grasping the rear legs above the hock joint while holding the front legs in the same hand. Hold the lamb close to your chest to stabilize the lamb or utilize a home-made lamb trough (figure 7.4). With a clean sharp knife or scissors, remove the bottom half of the scrotum. Squeeze the testicles out through the incision. Grasp the testicles. As you pull the testicles out, apply pressure at the base of the scrotum with the opposite hand. This will help prevent damage to the delicate tissues which hold the intestines in place. Damage to these tissues may result in a rupture. Some cultures prefer not to castrate male lambs. In these areas, males should be kept separate from females after four months of age to prevent them from breeding the ewes.

Tail Docking

Docking or removing the tails can be done at the same time as castration. This procedure is done only on certain breeds of sheep that have long tails. Fat tailed or short tailed sheep are generally not docked. The procedure is done to improve sanitation and prevent fly strike (the infestation with maggots). Removing the tails can be done with a sharp knife or a beveled hot iron. Hold the lamb as described above with the tail on a board or other hard surface. Hold the tail with one hand and cut with the other. The tail should

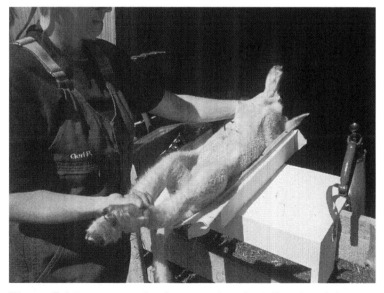

Figure 7.4 Proper restraint for removing the tail and testicles, as well as vaccinating.

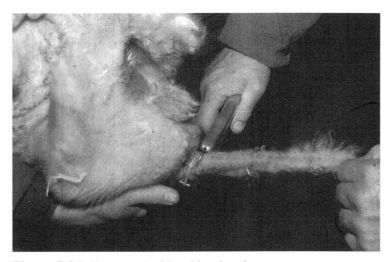

Figure 7.5 Tail removal with rubber band.

never be cut shorter than where the skin fold meets the tail (2-3 cm). Some bleeding will occur when using a knife. The artery that runs along the bottom side of the tail can be seared with a hot iron which will stop the bleeding. In some regions, specially made rubber bands are placed around the tail (figure 7.5). The tail then falls off 10-14 days later. If the ewes were not vaccinated against tetanus before lambing, the lambs should be vaccinated when the tails are docked.

The Lamb—Two Weeks to Weaning

Vaccinations

Vaccinations will depend on the area of the world and the diseases which are encountered at the particular locale. Vaccinate only for those conditions which are a problem in your particular locale.

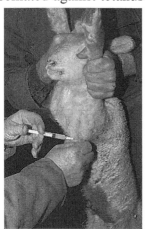

Figure 7.6
Vaccinating a lamb for enterotoxemia.

One of the most common diseases worldwide is enterotoxemia. Enterotoxemia vaccinations can be started at this time (figure 7.6).

Proper Injection Procedures

Injection procedures can affect both the quality of the pelt and the quality of the meat that comes from an animal. Improper techniques can result in pelt damage and can cause injection site abscesses or scar tissue that must be trimmed from the meat. When vaccinating livestock:

- Carefully read and follow product label instructions.

- Use sterile techniques and equipment.

- Store and handle vaccine properly.

- Use a clean needle to draw up medications or vaccines from the bottle. Never draw up medications or vaccines with a needle that has been used for an injection.

- Use a clean, sharp needle to inject the sheep. Never use dirty, dull or bent needles.

- Vaccinate only healthy, well-nourished animals. Proper nutrition is essential as a lack of protein and minerals in the diet will reduce the protective response by the animal.

- Never inject wet sheep. The injection site should be clean and dry as moisture can carry bacteria into the injection site.

- Use the smallest gauge needle possible. The smaller the needle, the smaller the hole in the skin, the less likely that dirt and bacteria will enter the wound and cause an abscess.

- Give injections under the skin (subcutaneously—SQ) rather than in the muscle (intramuscularly—IM), if permitted to do so per label directions. Subcutaneous injections cause less damage to the meat. However, some vaccines and medications must be injected into the muscle to be effective.

- Avoid giving injections in the rear leg and loin areas as these areas produce the most valuable cuts of meat. Give injections in the neck (SQ or IM) or in the woolless area behind the elbow (SQ) whenever possible.

- Follow label requirements for withholding time before slaughter.

- Wash syringes in soapy water after each use. Make sure that all traces of cleaning solution have been removed before syringes are reused.

Parasite Control
The control of both internal and external parasites is very important to healthy production and should begin during this stage of life. Refer to the section on parasite control for further information.

Adult Sheep

Vaccinating
See guidelines under the lamb section above.

Deworming
Depending on the form available, deworming medications can be given by injection or orally as a pill or liquid. The most common method is called drenching, which involves administering a dose of liquid by mouth. If only a few animals are being treated, the dose can be measured out in a syringe and squirted into the sheep's mouth. To treat a large flock, a drenching gun is used. This allows the calculated dose to be given using an automatic syringe attached to a reservoir of medication. Care must be taken to give the medication slowly to prevent choking. When a drenching gun is used, it must not be placed too far into the back of the throat or injury can occur. When calculating the dosages for deworming a large flock of sheep, calculate the dosage for the heaviest sheep in the flock IF all animals in the flock are close in size and stature. This will avoid under dosing which leads to parasite resistance.

Figure 7.7 Foot trimming.

Foot Trimming

The hoof of the sheep grows continuously, similar to the human fingernail. If it is not worn down, it becomes overgrown causing infections and lameness. Sheep that travel long distances or live on rough terrain rarely need their feet trimmed. Sheep that are confined or graze on wet pastures, however, may require foot trimming once or twice a year. Shears that are made for this purpose are the easiest to use. Alternatively, pruning shears, tin snips or a sharp knife can be used to trim away hoof that has curled under or tissue that is loose. If the sheep is set up on its rump, it will hold relatively still, facilitating handling of the feet.

Figure 7.8 If the sheep is set up on its rump, it will hold relatively still.

Restraining

To set a sheep up on its rump, grasp the sheep under the chin with one hand. Place the other hand on the rump. With the sheep against your legs, rotate the head and neck of the sheep away from your body while applying downward pressure on the rump. The sheep will sit down so you can set it up between your legs as shown (figure 7.8).

Section 8

Management for Fiber Production

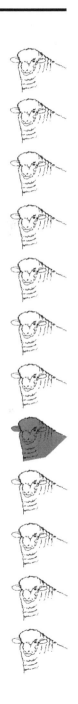

MANAGEMENT FOR FIBER PRODUCTION

Characteristics of Wool

One of the primary reasons for raising sheep is their abundant production of wool. Depending on the breed, a wooled sheep can produce from 2-15 kg of wool per year. The quality of the wool depends on its characteristics such as fiber length, fiber diameter and crimp, or waviness (figure 8.1). Fine wool has a very small fiber diameter while course wool has a larger diameter and tends to have longer fibers. Good wool production requires adequate nutrition and healthy sheep. Sheep that have been ill or undernourished will have weak fibers that break easily.

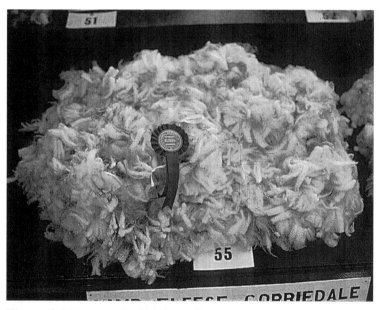

Figure 8.1 Fine wool of high quality.

Shearing

Clipping wool from the sheep is called shearing. It may be done with hand shears, which look like large scissors, or with electric shears. Most sheep are shorn once per year, although some with very long wool may be shorn twice per year. There are different styles of shearing. In some places, the shepherd shears the sheep while in other regions crews of shearers travel from flock to flock doing the shearing. Shearing time usually occurs when the weather begins to get warm in the spring. If adequate shelter is available, ewes can be shorn four to six weeks before lambing begins. If the animals are to be housed during a period of time, they can be shorn before being confined. This will keep the wool from becoming soiled by manure, feed and bedding. If severe cold, wet weather occurs following shearing, the sheep should be housed for a 10-14 day period. In most cases, they will then have enough regrowth of wool to protect them from the elements. Alternatively, a small amount of wool can be left on the animals for protection from the weather.

To prepare for shearing:

- Set up a handling area where the sheep can be confined and easily caught.

- Clear a sheltered area where the shearers can work.

- Make sure all the necessary equipment is available.

- Have a clean place in which to put the wool.

- Line up plenty of helpers to handle the sheep and wool.

- If wool is to be sold, ask the buyers how they want it prepared.

While shearing is taking place, be sure to:

- Keep the sheep dry.

- Treat shearing cuts with an antiseptic to prevent infection.

- Shear white sheep first and keep white wool separate from colored wool.

- Shear sick sheep and sheep with swellings and abscesses last.

- Store dirty wool separate from clean wool.

- Put wool in a clean, dry place until it is processed or sold.

Producing High Quality Wool

High quality wool is, above all, clean wool. Contamination with vegetable matter such as burrs or manure, chemicals like paint or other materials like plastic twine all reduce the usefulness of the wool. Sheep kept on pasture or grazed on rangelands tend to have the cleanest wool. Pastures may need to be cleared of weeds if weed seeds contaminate the wool. Housed sheep tend to accumulate bedding materials, feed and manure in their wool. Feeders that prevent the sheep from pulling hay out onto one another's backs will reduce contamination. In addition, feeding arrangements should not require that feed be thrown over the backs of the sheep.

Genetic improvement of wool characteristics can be made quite rapidly. Once the needs of the market are determined, males with superior wool characteristics can be selected to upgrade the wool qualities of the flock. Fiber diameter, fiber length, color and texture of the wool can all be affected through genetic selection programs.

Figure 8.2 Producing and handling high quality wool.

Even the best wool can be ruined by improper handling. It should be kept clean and dry and protected from sunlight, dampness and insects. If plastic bags are used to store wool, they should not be closed at the top as they tend to trap moisture. Wool sacks should not be stored on the ground for the same reason.

Marketing

Many small flock owners use all of their wool for household purposes. It is made into clothing, blankets, ropes and carpets. The excess wool or the finished products can be sold at local markets for additional household income. In some communities, groups of producers, often women, meet at a central location and produce woolen items for resale. The income is then divided among the workers. This is an especially effective way of marketing in regions where tourism flourishes. Owners of large flocks usually sell raw wool to a wool buyer who transports it to a factory for processing. Small flock owners can also combine their wool into larger lots and sell it this way. No matter which marketing method is used, it is important to consider the needs of the consumer when handling and processing the wool. This will ensure the highest possible financial return.

Figure 8.3 Spinning wool to make clothing.

Section 9

Producing Healthy Sheep

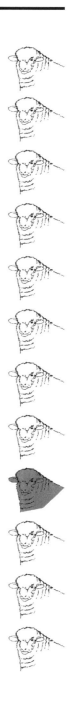

PRODUCING HEALTHY SHEEP

Diseases can occur from many different causes. These include improper nutrition, failure of internal organ functions, injury, infection, poisons or cancer. This section will include a brief description of the common ailments of sheep.

Respiratory Tract

The respiratory tract starts at the nostrils and carries oxygen rich air deep into the lungs where the blood exchanges the carbon dioxide for a new supply of oxygen. Oxygen in the air is what supports combustion for the fire in our stove or the wood we burn. The same is true in the body. Oxygen supports the combustion of carbohydrates, fat and protein in the body producing energy. The byproduct of producing energy in the body is carbon dioxide. The blood circulates throughout the body supplying oxygen to the cells and picking up the carbon dioxide that has been produced by cell metabolism. The blood passes through the kidney and liver which remove some of the byproducts of combustion. The blood vessels carrying the products of combustion are called veins which return the blood to the heart which in turn pumps it through the lungs where the oxygen exchange takes place. The area of the lung where the oxygen exchange occurs is called alveoli. These alveoli are like a bunch of grapes, all connected together by larger stems and branches, the bronchi and trachea. The inhaled air enters the nostril and passes some spiral structures called turbinates. These structures aid in purifying the air on its way to the lungs. The next destination is the pharyngeal and laryngeal area where the voice box is located. At this point the air enters the trachea. The trachea is lined with cells that have fringe-like projections called cilia. These cells act to trap dust and small particles and sweep them back toward the outside, keeping a clean air supply to the alveoli. The trachea divides into branches called bronchi. These further branch numerous times supplying each cluster of alveoli with clean oxygen rich air.

There are numerous conditions that can harm the cells along the passageway. Any interference with the passage of oxygen rich air to the alveoli reduces the capacity for combustion within the cells of the body. This is like burning a candle in a jar with the lid tightened. As soon as the flame has burned all of the oxygen, the candle dies. The same is true in the body. Therefore, any disease process that limits the oxygen exchange decreases the productivity of the animal.

When examining a sheep with respiratory conditions, begin by making some general observations:

1) Is the animal breathing with an open mouth or a closed mouth?
2) Does the animal have a nasal discharge? If so, is the discharge clear or cloudy; are there any streaks of blood in the discharge?
3) Palpate the area of the larynx. Are there any enlargements or abscesses that may be restricting the passage of air?
4) Does the animal have a fever?
5) Is the respiration normal or rapid?
6) Examine the mucous membranes. Is the animal anemic (are the membranes around the eyes or the gums pale)?

Restriction of air passage through the nostrils can be caused by tumors back in the nasal passageway. This is characterized by difficult breathing as sheep do not normally do open mouth breathing. For this condition, there is no treatment. Nose bots also restrict the passage of air. These are characterized by a runny nose that may have streaks of blood in the mucous. The sheep will often sneeze trying to expel the nose bot larvae. Treatment with Ivermectin will usually solve this problem. Fortunately, sheep do not usually have problems in the area of the larynx (voice box) as is characteristic of diphtheria or inflammation of the trachea due to Infectious Bovine Rhinotracheitis in cattle. Sometimes the lesions of caseous lymphadenitis can involve the laryngeal area causing restriction of air passage. This can be detected by palpating the area and feeling the enlarged abscess. Care must be taken in opening and draining these abscesses as major blood vessels are in the immediate area.

The above conditions restrict the movement of air in the upper passages but do not cause a fever. If the sheep has a fever, it is usually due to a bacterial infection. The primary bacterial infection of the lungs is caused by *Pasteurella*. Ovine progressive pneumonia is caused by a virus but has a slow process which replaces the oxygen exchanging alveoli with other tissue cells. This type of pneumonia restricts the oxygen exchange causing the animal to become thin and weak but does not produce a fever. This condition does not affect lambs or younger sheep as does pasteurellosis.

Rapid breathing may indicate a number of conditions. One of the first considerations is bacterial pneumonia. The other common cause of rapid respiration is anemia or loss of blood. This is commonly seen with *Haemonchus* (a stomach worm) infestations. When examining the sheep for any condition, one should always examine the mucous membranes for indications of blood loss. Rapid breathing may be normal when the air temperature is high. In cases of high air temperatures, the entire group of sheep will have rapid respiration as opposed to the rapid respiration of a single sick animal in the group.

The specific diseases mentioned here are covered in greater detail later in this chapter.

Digestive Tract

The digestive tract starts with the lips, continues through the body, and ends at the anus. The primary function of the digestive tract is to take in food and grind it so that the digestive juices and microorganisms can change it into a form that can be absorbed by the cells lining the intestines. The blood (circulatory system) picks up these nutrients and delivers them to the cells. The nutrients are mixed with oxygen and burned to produce energy for maintenance and production.

The digestive system of the sheep has the ability to utilize a vast variety of feeds which are converted and utilized in the production of meat, milk and fiber. As with the respiratory tract, numerous factors can affect efficiency of the digestive tract and its ability to change feeds into production. Problems with the digestive tract are expressed in a variety of ways. Most problems are associated with a lack of production. The animal is either thin, has low milk and fiber production or lacks energy. To identify problems with the digestive tract, one must:

1) First determine if adequate and balanced nutrients, including water, are available to the animal.
2) Consider the age of the animal. Starvation is one of the major causes of death in baby lambs. Scours or diarrhea is a common condition affecting newborn and young animals that have been deprived of adequate colostrums or are housed in an unsanitary environment. Sometimes scours, commonly referred to as milk scours, can be due to an overload of colostrums which is not harmful. Milk scours occurs early in life when the colostrum acts as a laxative or purging agent that cleans the digestive tract. In these cases, the young lamb remains bright and alert. Other forms of scours that occur during the first few hours of life are due to infectious agents. Viruses (rotovirus and coronavirus) and bacteria (*E. coli*) can cause diarrhea and death in the first few hours of life. Other bacterial agents, such as *Salmonella* usually affect older lambs. As sheep mature, internal parasites are the most common agents causing diarrhea and should be one of the first things considered. A chronic diarrhea in older sheep that is not cleared up by deworming practices may indicate Johne's disease.
3) Observe the animal eating. Can the animal grasp and chew its food? Sore mouth lesions in lambs or bad teeth in older animals may prevent the animal from picking up feed and properly chewing it.
4) Examine the mucous membranes. Is the animal anemic (are the membranes around the eyes or the gums pale)? Anemia may indicate parasitism.
5) Examine the animal for any abnormal swellings that might indicate a rupture.
6) Abscesses from caseous lymphadenitis can cause obstructions anywhere along the digestive tract, but are difficult to identify ante-mortem. These animals may show chronic weight loss in spite of treatment for worms or other things.

7) Take a look at the feces—note its color and consistency. Nutrition can affect the nature of the feces. In the young lamb, a very watery feces may indicate a *Colibacillosis* type of scours. A yellowish scours in a very young lamb may be due to an overload of colostrums (milk scours). However, a yellowish diarrhea in older lambs may indicate Salmonellosis or grain overload. A dark fluid feces, with streaks of blood in older lambs, may indicate coccidiosis.

The above conditions are presented in greater detail in the remainder of this chapter.

Metabolic Diseases

Metabolic diseases are caused by imbalances in the chemical makeup of the body. The most common ones are listed below.

Pregnancy Disease—Pregnancy disease or twin lamb disease happens when two or more fetuses are developing during the last part of pregnancy. Seventy-five percent of the fetal development occurs in the last six weeks of gestation. As the fetuses grow, they place increasing demands on the ewe for nutrition. If the ewe does not have an adequate supply of nutrients, especially energy; body fat and muscle will be broken down and converted to energy for the fetuses. The byproduct of this breakdown becomes toxic to the ewe causing weakness, incoordination and eventually coma and death. The very thin ewe and the over fat ewe are very susceptible to this problem. Any disruption of feed intake or quality or quantity of feed during this period of high demand may cause the disease. The ewe should be kept in good body condition. The amount of energy in the diet should be gradually increased during the last six weeks of gestation.

Diagnosis—Ewe in late gestation that separates from the flock, becomes depressed and slow, eventually goes down and has difficulty rising. Temperature is normal or low. Appetite may be depressed.

Treatment—Give high energy feed. Force feed with a high energy feed if she won't eat on her own. Injections of vitamin B complex may be helpful.

Figure 9.1 Ewe down with pregnancy toxemia, also known as twin lamb paralysis.

Prevention—Provide good nutrition, water and exercise during the last six weeks of gestation. Keep the ewes in good body condition during late gestation. Increase the energy content of the ration gradually during late pregnancy.

Hypomagnesemia (Grass Tetany)—Grass tetany occurs when the diet is deficient in magnesium. The condition can occur in very late gestation, at about the time of parturition (lambing) or during early lactation (milking). The condition occurs when there is new lush grass which is low in magnesium. This usually happens during the change in seasons when new grass or small grains, such as wheat or rye, are growing rapidly. The low magnesium level in the animal affects the nervous system. The animal will become very excitable. Nervous twitches develop. Walking becomes uncoordinated. The animal may go down with the legs in spasms or convulsions. Saliva may pour from the mouth.

Diagnosis—Diagnosis is made from the history of grazing new lush grass or grains, late pregnancy or early lactation, nervousness and incoordination. The temperature will be normal unless the animal has gone into convulsions or other extreme activity due to the nervousness. Extreme excitability to noise or other distractions is common.

Treatment—A recommended treatment is 50-100 ml of a saturated solution of magnesium sulfate injected under the skin or administered rectally. Treatment is effective if given early.

Prevention—Limit the amount of grazing on lush fast growing grasses or supply a mineral mix that is high in magnesium. This mix only needs to be given during that time when the grasses are young and fast growing. Providing some hay to ewes on small grain pastures will also help prevent hypomagnesemia.

Hypocalcemia (Milk Fever)—Milk fever is caused by low blood calcium concentrations and is usually seen at lambing time when the ewe is producing a lot of milk, or shortly before lambing. Calcium plays a key role in muscle contraction, and the conduction of nerve impulses. When blood calcium is low, the ewe will lie down and appear very lethargic. If this happens before lambing, uterine and abdominal muscles may not be able to contract making delivery impossible. If the condition occurs following lambing, the ewe may become depressed, weak and unable to stand because the muscles cannot contract. The condition can be caused by mineral imbalances in the diet.

Diagnosis—A diagnosis is made from a clinical history of recent lambing with high milk production along with depression

Figure 9.2 Milk fever. Low blood calcium will make the ewe appear lethargic.

and a down ewe that is unable to rise. The temperature will be normal to subnormal. The animal is not excitable as seen in hypomagnesemia.

Treatment—Give 50-100 ml of calcium borogluconate solution in the vein or under the skin.

Prevention—Avoid the stress of sudden changes of feed, moving long distances or shearing near lambing time. Any stressful condition depletes calcium from the system. Provide adequate but not excessive calcium and magnesium in the diet.

Polioencephalomalacia (Polio)—Polio is a softening of the gray matter of the brain resulting in blindness, depression and incoordination. This condition occurs in older lambs and adult sheep. Changes in the microbial makeup in the rumen result in signs of a thiamine (B vitamin) deficiency. It is usually associated with a rapid change in diet. It may also be associated with certain plants or feeds and water that are high in sulfates. Lambs that are fed large amounts of beet pulp from the processing plant may develop the disease.

Diagnosis—Clinical symptoms are blindness, incoordination, and depression. The sheep may be down and unable to stand and paddle the legs involuntarily. The head may be held back as if the animal is gazing at the stars. The sheep may become comatose and

Figure 9.3 Lamb with polioencephalomalacia.

live for a number of days or die within a day or two. Response to thiamine treatment suggests a diagnosis of polio. The diagnosis may be confirmed by examination of microscopic sections of the brain.

Treatment—Affected sheep should be isolated and provided appropriate nursing care during treatment and convalescence. Administration of 10 mg/kg of thiamine hydrochloride twice daily for 2 to 3 days is an effective treatment. This should be given in the muscle or in the vein. Recovery may take several days so water and nutrients may need to be given by a stomach tube.

Prevention—If there are a number of cases, one should consider changing the feed and water sources if possible. Any changes in the diet should be done gradually over a 7-10 day period.

Urolithiasis (Water Belly)—Urolithiasis, the formation of urinary stones, develops when there are mineral imbalances in the diet. Male sheep have a relatively small urethra which can become blocked if urinary stones occur.

Diagnosis—Affected male sheep (intact or castrated) will be seen to strain with a hunched back. Urine may dribble from the end of the penis, or no urine at all may be passed. The straining may be mistaken for constipation. The animal will quit eating and drinking and in the early stages is restless, frequently lying down and standing back up. If the urethra ruptures, urine leaks out into the abdominal tissues, hence the common name "water belly". After 24-48 hours, the animal will become weak, eventually go into a coma and die.

Treatment—Treatment involves surgical removal of the blockage to save the sheep. If the blockage is at the very tip of the penis, the thin, wormlike projection (urethral process) can be snipped off. Removal of this tissue does not affect the breeding ability of a ram.

Prevention—Prevention of urolithiasis requires careful balancing of the mineral content of the diet. Ideally, the calcium to phosphorous ratio should be between 2:1 and 3:1. Grains tend to be high in phosphorous and low in calcium while legumes are the opposite. Sheep should be encouraged to drink plenty of water which will aid in flushing out the urinary tract. If cases of urolithiasis occur in a flock, salt may be added to the feed at a concentration of 0.5-2% to stimulate water consumption.

Digestive Disorders

Bloat—Because of the gas that is produced in the rumen during digestion, sheep are prone to bloat. If the gas cannot escape, the rumen becomes distended, putting pressure on the internal organs and eventually causing death.

Diagnosis—Signs of bloat include swelling of the abdomen on the left side behind the ribs, difficulty breathing and weakness. The affected animal eventually lies down and death soon follows.

Treatment—Treatment involves passing a tube down the throat into the rumen to allow escape of the excess gas. In some cases, the bloat is caused by a buildup of foam in the rumen. Administering several ounces of vegetable oil will help breakdown the foam and relieve the bloat. In an emergency, a trocar, large needle or knife can be used to puncture the rumen between the last rib and the hip ON THE LEFT SIDE OF THE BODY to allow escape of the excess gas.

Prevention—Prevention of bloat requires careful attention to feeding practices. Large amounts of grain should not be fed without an adaptation period of 7-10 days. Round objects like apples, potatoes and onions can become lodged in the throat and prevent the burping of gas. Legumes can cause the development of foamy bloat. When grazing fields of fresh alfalfa or clover, keep hay available and make sure the animals do not get hungry and then overeat the legume.

Grain Overload—Excessive fermentation of high energy feeds, which results in an acid environment, can cause damage to the lining of the rumen and death of the fermenting microbes that live in the rumen. When this occurs, the digestive tract shuts down, the sheep absorbs poisons from the rumen, and death may occur.

Diagnosis—The affected animal becomes lethargic and weak, may have diarrhea, and stops eating and drinking. Death may occur suddenly, or the sheep may linger for several days before it dies.

Treatment—Treatment includes giving an antacid like baking soda (approximately 4 heaping spoonfuls dissolved in water), water to prevent dehydration and mineral oil to purge the digestive tract. These are given by mouth—preferably through a tube leading directly into the rumen. If available, 10 ml of penicillin can also be given orally.

Prevention—To prevent grain overload, keep feeds in closed storage areas that are not accessible to livestock. Make any changes in diet gradually over a 7-10 day period.

CAUTION—Sheep, goats and cattle with rabies can show signs similar to those described for bloat or grain overload. **If rabies is present in your area, consult an animal health professional before putting your hands into a sick animal's mouth or throat.** Exposure to the saliva of a rabid animal can transmit rabies to humans.

Figure 9.4 Depression resulting from acidosis or grain overload.

Toxic Plants—Each region of the world has plants that are poisonous when eaten by livestock. It is not possible to describe them in a handbook of this nature. Experienced livestock producers will have knowledge of the dangerous plants in their localities. The best way to prevent livestock poisoning is to provide the animals with adequate sources of safe feed. Most cases of poisoning occur when animals are kept in areas without adequate feed and become hungry. For example, flocks kept on rangelands after the grasses are gone may begin to eat poisonous plants. They should, instead, be removed from the area and fed harvested feeds or be moved to an area where feed is adequate.

Photosensitization—Photosensitization can result from a variety of factors, including chronic liver disease, dietary substances, fungal toxins, drugs, and on occasion, genetic defects. In most cases, however, photosensitization is associated with specific plants that contain photoreactive pigments that destroy the liver's ability to detoxify the toxic substances that cause the photosensitive reaction. When a number of sheep are affected with photosensitivity, plants are a strong consideration. When plants are involved, it is important to identify, and if possible, eliminate the source of the problem.

Injuries—Injuries can occur any time from birth to maturity. Injuries at birth can be caused by rough handling of the newborn by the shepherd or by the mother when she paws at the lamb trying to get it to stand and nurse. If the facility is too small, the mother may lie or step on the lamb. Keep all dogs and other unfamiliar things away from the new mother as during her excitement and distraction; she may injure the young lamb.

Sheep often sustain injuries from sharp objects, sticks, tree branches and other objects which are in the pastures or around confinement areas. To prevent these types of injuries, one should remove all obstacles from the pasture or premises that could possibly damage the sheep. Most injuries to adult sheep happen when they are being worked in improperly constructed facilities. Gentle and quiet handling will prevent most injuries. Taking time to acquaint the sheep with the facilities where they will be worked will reduce the risk of injury.

Snake Bites—There are numerous venomous snakes throughout the world which cause animal, as well as human, suffering.

The venom from each poisonous snake has different components that cause the problem. The poisons damage the nervous system; cause an allergic response, cause hemorrhage and necrosis of tissue. Some bites cause extreme swelling and pain, while others cause respiratory failure and death. For anti-venom to be effective, it must be for the specific type of snake involved and be given within a couple of hours following the bite. Supportive treatment—making the animal comfortable as possible—will help. If the bite results in necrosis and dead tissue; the dead tissue should be removed and antibiotics given to prevent the development of other infections.

Infectious Diseases

The infectious process is dependent upon a number of links that complete the chain and cause a disease. Each step depends upon the successful completion of the preceding one. If this chain is broken at any of its many links, disease will not develop. The links of the chain are:

An Infectious Agent such as bacteria, virus or fungus.

A reservoir or source such as another sick sheep or a contaminated environment.

A mode of escape from the reservoir. For example, in cases of pneumonia, the escape is via the respiratory tract. In cases of mastitis, the escape is via the milk. In cases of diarrhea, the escape is via the feces. Organisms that cause abscesses escape when the abscess breaks and drains. Organisms that cause abortion escape with the uterine discharges.

A mode of transmission from the reservoir to the new host (sheep). Transmission in cases of scours or diarrhea is usually via contaminated feed or water. Transmission of pneumonia is usually via direct contact or via the air when another animal coughs or sneezes and discharges the organisms in small droplets or aerosols. Organisms that cause abortions are discharged and contaminate the feed or are consumed directly.

A mode of entry into the new host. Organisms that cause pneumonia usually enter via the respiratory tract although some, like the pasteurella organism, can be ingested or swallowed. Organisms that cause diarrhea enter via ingestion of contaminated feeds. Organisms that cause abscesses enter through puncture wounds or sometimes, as in the case of caseous lymphadenitis, they can be ingested. The organisms that cause abortions enter with ingestion of contaminated feed.

A susceptible host. If all of the previous events have taken place and the new host is resistant, disease will not occur. Vaccinating the sheep for different conditions such as sore mouth or tetanus will increase the resistance and often protect the sheep from disease. Nutrition plays a tremendous role in increasing the natural resistance of the host. Sheep that are undernourished, especially those on low protein feeds, will have lowered resistance and be more susceptible to disease. Heavily parasitized animals will also be more susceptible to disease. Colostrum, the first milk produced by the ewe, contains antibodies to protect the newborn lamb from infection. It is very important that the lamb receive this protection immediately after birth.

Preventing Infectious Diseases

Agent
We can help prevent disease by starting with or keeping only healthy sheep. This is often difficult as some sheep that appear healthy may be carriers of an organism that will produce disease in a susceptible sheep. An example would be pasteurella pneumonia. The mother may carry the organism in her tonsils and spread it to her lamb early in life. If the lamb is stressed and weak from the cold or from ammonia in the pen, it will come down with pneumonia. The same can be true of diarrhea which can be caused by bacteria or viruses. Many disease organisms may be carried by the normal sheep but not cause a problem until the animal is stressed or weakened resulting in a lowered resistance. Sheep with foot rot, abscesses, mastitis, and other obvious conditions should not be allowed in the flock.

Reservoir or Source

The sick animal is one source of the infectious agent. The most important reservoir is the healthy carrier that harbors the disease organism but does not show any signs of illness. With some diseases, like Brucellosis, we can detect the carrier animal with a blood test. The animals that test positive can then be removed from the herd, thus eliminating the reservoir of the agent.

Escape

Depending on the disease, the infectious organism escapes from the animal by way of a number of different routes. Pneumonia escapes via the respiratory tract, scours via the digestive tract, abortion diseases via the genital tract, abscesses via open draining wounds, and mastitis via the milk. Once the animal becomes infected, it is difficult to prevent escape of the organism.

Transmission

Good husbandry is the most important factor in preventing transmission of disease organisms. Isolation of sick animals from healthy ones is the first step toward preventing transmission. Cleaning and sanitizing the area where sick animals have been helps prevent transmission of the organism. Burning or burying contaminated bedding and infected materials, such as aborted materials, is extremely important in preventing transmission. Cats are carriers of toxoplasmosis, an organism that causes abortion. It is transmitted via the cat feces contaminating the feed sources. Transmission is prevented by keeping the cats from defecating in the feed. Disease organisms can also be transmitted on dirty equipment and on the shepherd's hands. Small droplets of moisture expelled by coughing or sneezing can also carry the disease organisms. Such is the mode of transmission of pneumonia.

Entry

It is impossible to prevent the entry of organisms via the respiratory or digestive tract as the animal must breath and eat. Disease organisms can be introduced by the shepherd when giving shots with dirty syringes or needles. When assisting the ewe in delivering a lamb, extreme cleanliness must be maintained to prevent introduction of disease organisms. Caseous lymphadenitis organisms are often introduced from shearing wounds. These wounds must be thoroughly cleaned and disinfected to prevent entry of infectious organisms. Organisms causing "naval ill" or "joint ill" enter via the umbilical cord. Prevent entry by treating the umbilical cord with iodine disinfectant at birth.

Susceptible Host

The infective agent may get into the animal, but infection does not always occur. The animal has many defense mechanisms. Normal skin is the first line of defense which resists the invasion of infective organisms. If taken in by mouth, the saliva will destroy some organisms. Further down the digestive tract, the stomach acids will destroy some organisms. If the organism passes though the wall of the intestine, the white blood cells will attack and kill some organisms. Products from the immune system which circulate in the blood or are attached to cells will also neutralize some organisms or toxins.

How to Improve Resistance

All of these protective mechanisms are supported by good nutrition and freedom from stress. Consumption of colostrum by the lamb is its first line of defense against infectious agents. Resistance of the sheep can be increased by vaccination. Vaccinations work best in animals that are in good health and have an adequate diet of protein and minerals. An adequate diet can be provided from the resources that you have available. Depending on your location, vaccines may be available for:

Tetanus
Soremouth
Foot Rot
Enterotoxemia
Foot and Mouth Disease
Sheep Pox
Campylobacter
Bluetongue

Agent
Susceptibility
Resivor
Entry
Escape
Transmission

* Break the weakest link * to prevent

Caseous Lymphadenitis
Toxoplasmosis

The type of vaccine needed will vary with the conditions present in the immediate locality. If the condition does not exist in the area or is not a problem, do not spend the money to vaccinate. The timing for giving vaccinations will depend on the disease and the time of the year that the disease is most prevalent. When vaccinating, make certain to read the instructions and follow them. Use clean equipment and a sanitary procedure. Always use a sharp needle as dull needles will often carry in wool and dirt causing an abscess.

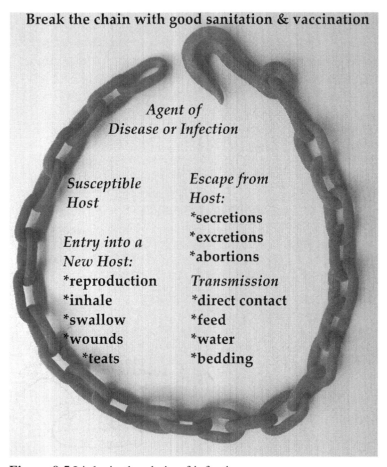

Break the chain with good sanitation & vaccination

Agent of Disease or Infection

Susceptible Host

Entry into a New Host:
*reproduction
*inhale
*swallow
*wounds
*teats

Escape from Host:
*secretions
*excretions
*abortions

Transmission
*direct contact
*feed
*water
*bedding

Figure 9.5 Links in the chain of infectious process.

REMEMBER TO:

- **Start with healthy animals.**

- **Use genetic selection of disease resistant animals.**

- **Isolate any newly introduced animals for 30 days.**

- **Provide good nutrition with adequate protein and minerals.**

- **Provide a clean environment.**

- **Do not overcrowd.**

- **Isolate any sick animals.**

- **Burn or bury any contaminated/infectious material.**

- **Keep the feed and water clean.**

- **Avoid stress conditions.**

- **Treat regularly for internal and external parasites.**

- **Provide adequate shelter.**

- **Keep shelter areas clean.**

- **Ensure that lambs get adequate colostrums.**

- Don't change your nutrition quickly!

Viral Infections

Viral infections are caused by viruses. Viruses are minute infectious agents that can multiply only within animal cells. They cause diseases by damaging the cells of the host animal. Medications are generally ineffective against viral diseases, and treatment involves supportive care. The following list of viral diseases includes some of the more common ones. There are others that may occur in your

— 103 —

region. Contact local health officials for assistance in the diagnosis of disease outbreaks.

Ovine Progressive Pneumonia (OPP) or Maedi-Visna—As the name, Ovine Progressive Pneumonia, implies, it is a slow progressive pneumonia that progressively destroys functional lung tissue. The disease condition is contracted early in life when the virus is transmitted via the mother's milk to the newborn lamb. OPP can also be transmitted by direct contact from sheep to sheep. There are various forms of the disease caused by the same OPP virus:

1. pneumonia also called maedi,
2. mastitis called hard bag,
3. arthritis, and
4. encephalitis called visna.

The pneumonia form is different from that caused by bacteria. The animal does not develop a fever and become depressed and sick, but rather slowly loses condition as breathing becomes difficult. This may take months or years. The condition usually becomes noticeable after the animals are more than 3 or 4 years of age. The mastitis form is also different from that caused by bacteria. The udder does not become hot, red and tender to the touch as in bacterial mastitis. The udder appears like there should be milk, but due to white blood cells that surround and close off the milk ducts, the milk is trapped in the udder. Thus, this form of mastitis is known as "hard bag". The arthritis form usually affects the knee joints causing the joints to swell, and the animal becomes lame. The nervous form causes incoordination in the back legs. The animal has difficulty tracking. The back legs track off to the side when the animal walks. One or all of these forms may be present in the same animal. There is no treatment, and the condition continues to progress as the name implies. There are blood tests available for diagnosis if a laboratory is available and capable of conducting the test. Prevention is by purchasing animals free from the disease. If there is a problem in the flock, **DO NOT** keep any of the offspring from the infected mother for replacements.

Sheep Pox—The sheep pox virus causes red raised areas on the skin which develop into open sores. The animals have a fever, and since internal organs can also be affected, may die. Sheep pox occurs primarily in Eastern Europe, Asia and Africa. Vaccines are available in some regions.

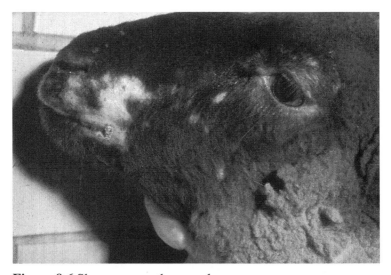

Figure 9.6 Sheep pox on the muzzle.

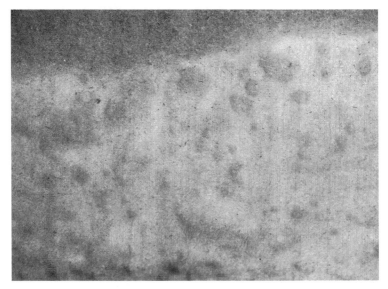

Figure 9.7 Generalized lesions of sheep pox.

Soremouth—This virus is related to the pox virus but causes less severe disease. Usually lambs are affected and have raised crusty sores on their mouth and nose. They are reluctant to eat and will lose weight. Sores heal without treatment over a period of weeks. **This virus is contagious to humans, who may develop painful sores on the hands or arms.** Following infection, sheep become immune. Vaccines are sometimes used to expose lambs to the virus by causing lesions to develop in a less painful place such as the inside of the ear or under the tail. Soremouth lesions can be treated topically with a mixture of glycerin and strong (7%) iodine or chlorhexidine ointment or solution. Topical applications of injectable vitamin B-12 may also assist in healing.

Figure 9.8 Soremouth lesions on the lips.

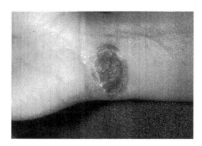

Figure 9.9 Soremouth (orf) lesion on the human arm.

Bluetongue—This virus is transmitted by the *Culicoides* species of gnat and, therefore, occurs during the height of insect activity. Infected animals develop a fever, oral ulcers and swollen lips and ears. If infected during early pregnancy, ewes may resorb the fetuses or give birth to deformed lambs. Infected rams may be infertile for up to 60 days following infection. Vaccines are used in regions of the world where bluetongue occurs (Africa, North America, Asia and Europe). Good nursing care and supportive treatment are also helpful.

Figure 9.10 Early bluetongue.
Note the swollen ears and muzzle.

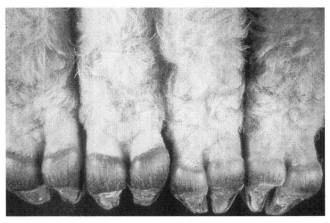

Figure 9.11 Bluetongue. Inflammation of the coronary band at the top of the hoof causes lameness.

Foot and Mouth Disease—Foot and mouth virus causes painful sores on the feet and in the mouth of infected sheep. Affected animals stop eating and lose weight. They are unable to graze and cannot keep up with the flock when herded. In many regions of the world where this infection occurs (Europe, Asia, Africa and South America), vaccines are available and may be supplied free of charge by the government.

Bacterial Infections

Bacterial infections are caused by single-celled organisms that invade the animal's body and damage host cells. Antibiotics are effective against some bacterial diseases. Like the viral diseases, there are many that occur in local areas that may not be described here. Contact local health officials for help in the diagnosis of these diseases.

Caseous Lymphadenitis—This infection is caused by a bacterium (Corynebacterium pseudotuberculosis) that creates abscesses (pus filled pockets). These abscesses may be found externally under the skin, may involve the lymph nodes, or may

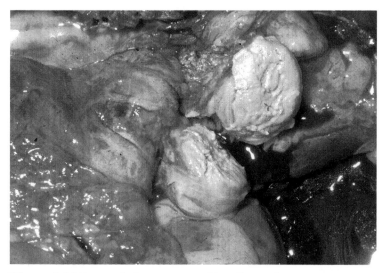

Figure 9.12 Internal abscess caused by *Corynebacterium pseudotuberculosis*.

be internal, especially in the lungs and liver. If the abscesses are external, they will be seen as gradually enlarging swellings that will eventually break open and drain pus. Animals with internal abscesses will gradually lose weight and become weak. The pus contains many bacteria that can survive in the environment and infect other animals. Goats can be infected and occasionally humans. Animals with external abscesses should be isolated from the rest of the flock. Ideally, they should be butchered, with areas around the abscesses trimmed away carefully. The remainder of the carcass is safe for consumption. If slaughter of the animal is not an option, then the abscess can be opened and drained. Discharged material and contaminated bedding should be burned or buried deeply. The abscess should be flushed out with an antiseptic (iodine or sodium hypochlorite [household chlorine bleach] diluted 1:40 with water) and the animal should be kept away from others until the abscess closes up. Antibiotics are not effective in this condition because the bacteria are inside the abscess and are walled off from the body. The disease is often transmitted

Figure 9.13 External abscess caused by *Corynebacterium pseudotuberculosis*.

from older animals to younger ones at shearing time. The organism may also enter through the digestive or respiratory tract. The flock should be shorn from youngest to oldest, and any animals with swellings or draining abscess should be shorn last. Shearing blades should be disinfected between animals and before use on another flock. Vaccines are available in some regions. They help to reduce the number of affected sheep but will not completely eradicate the disease.

Pasteurellosis—This bacterial disease (*Pasteurella multocida* or *Manheimia haemolytica*) is spread through coughing and nasal discharges. It causes pneumonia, especially in young animals, and may even result in the sudden death of apparently normal sheep. Adult animals are often resistant to the disease but may be carriers of the bacteria and pass it to the lambs. Treatment with antibiotics is sometimes effective if started early. However, affected animals may have permanent lung damage and often do not grow normally following recovery. Prevention involves providing good ventilation. This disease rarely affects grazing animals but is common among those kept inside buildings where ammonia fumes and damp or dusty conditions occur. Effective vaccines are being researched, but as yet, none are available.

Colibacillosis (Watery Mouth)—The bacteria that causes this disease (*Escherichia coli*) are commonly found in manure. While adult animals have immunity to its infection, young lambs are very susceptible and can develop a fatal infection. Lambs are usually infected shortly after birth, either by mouth or through the umbilical cord. An infected lamb becomes weak and depressed, stops nursing and will usually die within 24 hours. The lamb may salivate excessively; hence, the common English name for the disease is "watery mouth." If treated within the first hour or two, antibiotics may be effective. Prevention involves good sanitation. Lambs should be born in a clean, dry place, and the umbilicus should be dipped in iodine or dilute bleach. The wool around the ewe's udder should be trimmed so that the lamb does not suck on dirty wool when searching for the teat. The first milk from the ewe (colostrums) contains protective antibodies for the lamb so it is critical that the lamb nurse within the first 1-2 hours of life. If the lamb is unable to nurse, it should be fed colostrums (25 mls/kg body weight) from a bottle or by tube.

Dermatophilosis (Wool Rot)—The common English name for this disease is "wool rot." It occurs during wet weather when the bacterium (Dermatophilus congolensis) multiplies on the skin. Moist, red sores develop, and the wool becomes matted, eventually becoming loose and failing out. Affected sheep may be itchy and rub themselves. Clipping the wool around the infected spots and applying an antiseptic will promote healing. Treatment with injectable penicillin is also helpful.

Chlamydial Conjunctivitis (Pinkeye)—There are several organisms that can cause pinkeye in sheep. They are carried by flies from an infected animal to the rest of the flock. Sheep with pinkeye have excessive tearing and squinting. The lining of the eyelids and the tissue around the eyes becomes red and swollen. The cornea, the normally clear surface of the eye, becomes cloudy and affected animals may become blind. Sheep with pinkeye should

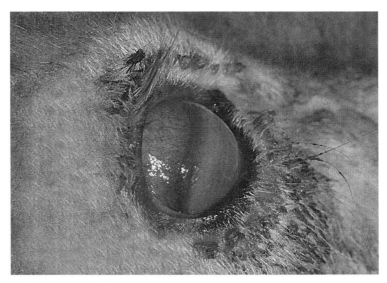

Figure 9.14 Chlamydial conjunctivitis or pinkeye.

be isolated from the rest of the flock and protected from direct sunlight. Antibiotic treatment with tetracycline eye ointment is helpful. In some cases, the entire flock is treated with injectable long-acting tetracycline. Most animals will recover without any permanent eye damage. Recovered sheep have an immunity that lasts approximately six months but may be infected gain after the immunity wear off.

The same strain of Chlamydia causing conjunctivitis may cause a polyarthritis. This is usually seen in lambs.

Figure 9.15 *C. polyarthritis.*

Bacterial Mastitis—Mastitis is a general term for inflammation of the mammary gland. There are many organisms that can cause mastitis. It commonly occurs either just after lambing or at weaning time when the milk is drying up. The first sign of mastitis is often hind leg lameness, since it is painful for the ewe to move the leg on the affected side. If she is nursing lambs, they will act hungry if the ewe does not allow them to nurse. When the udder is examined, the infected side will be hot, swollen and painful. The milk may appear watery or may contain clots. The ewe is often running a fever (normal temperature 100-103°F, 37-39°C). She will be lethargic and usually does not eat. Mastitis often follows stress or injury. Soremouth lesions on the teat end will allow bacteria into the gland causing mastitis. The most important treatment for bacterial mastitis is frequent milking out of the infected gland. This removes the bacteria and the poisons that they produce. The infected side should be milked out every two hours until the swelling is reduced, and the milk appears normal. If they are available, injectable antibiotics like penicillin can also be used. Aspirin (10 mg/kg) can be given to reduce the fever and inflammation. A ewe with mastitis may become extremely ill, requiring intensive veterinary care and even amputation of the udder. Some cases of mastitis are fatal. Even in cases where the ewe recovers, permanent damage to the gland usually occurs with loss of milk-producing capabilities. Prevention of mastitis requires good sanitation. Lambing should take place in a clean dry area. Milkers should wash and dry their hands before handling the teats, and if the teats are wet or muddy, they should also be washed and dried before milking. Watch the udder closely for the first few days after lambing. If the lambs are not nursing from both sides, the distended half should be milked out. Usually after the first few days the lambs will nurse from both teats. The udder of ewes whose lambs have been weaned should also be watched closely for excessive distention. When weaning lambs from high-producing ewes, it is a good practice to reduce feed and water to the ewes for 48 to 72 hours.

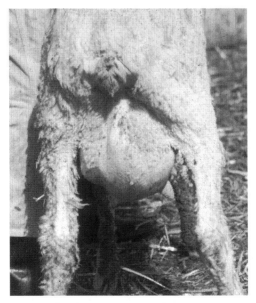

Figure 9.16 Mastitis.

Abortion Diseases

There are many different organisms that cause abortion, premature loss of the fetus, in sheep. Since many of them are contagious to humans, it is important to take extreme care in the handling of any aborted materials. Gloves should be worn when examining or disposing of the tissues. If tissues are not sent to a diagnostic lab, they should be burned or buried deeply. Pregnant women should NOT assist in the care of a flock in which abortions occur. Ewes that have aborted should be isolated from the rest of the flock for 10-14 days until vaginal discharge has stopped. This will reduce the risk of transmission to other pregnant ewes. Specific flock treatment for an abortion outbreak depends on the diagnosis of the cause by a veterinary diagnostic lab. It is not possible to determine the cause simply by looking at the tissues. If abortions occur in greater than 2% of the ewes, aborted fetuses and placentas (the sack that is passed with the fetus) should be kept cold and transported to a laboratory immediately. Even with laboratory testing, it may be difficult to determine the exact organism involved. Several of the organisms that cause abortions are sensitive to tetracycline antibiotics. Treatment of the entire flock with injections of long-acting tetracycline or tetracycline in the feed may reduce the number of abortions. Feed can become contaminated with feces and urine that contain abortion causing organisms. Feeding methods should minimize the potential feed contamination. Stores of grain and hay should be kept in areas that rodents, cats and other animals cannot enter.

Figure 9.17 Aborted fetus.

Brucellosis—There are several different brucellosis organisms. *Brucella melitensis* is the most serious of these in sheep because the disease can be transmitted to humans through dairy products and contact with aborted materials. Some countries have eradicated this disease. Ask local health officials if *B. melitensis* is present in your area. If it is, avoid the consumption of unpasteurized milk and yogurt and cheese made from unpasteurized milk. *B. melitensis* causes abortion in sheep and goats while *B. ovis* causes varying degrees of infertility in rams (male sheep). *B. ovis* has not been found to infect humans.

Contagious Footrot—Footrot is caused by the combination of two bacteria, one that lives in the soil and one that is present in infected sheep feet. The sheep become very lame, and there is a moist lesion between the toes near the heel. The infection progresses under the sole of the foot which becomes rotten with a strong putrid odor. Sheep with footrot have a difficult time keeping up with the flock and will sometimes lie down to eat. The incidence is usually greater during wet weather when the organisms are passed from one sheep to the next as they walk through wet or muddy ground. Communal watering holes are common sources of infection as are pens where sheep are confined.

Figure 9.18 Ewe with footrot.

Sheep with footrot should be separated from unaffected sheep. Their hooves should be trimmed to remove rotten tissue and an antiseptic solution applied. The best way to apply an antiseptic solution is to have the sheep stand in a footbath containing the solution for one hour. This should be repeated weekly for three weeks. Sheep that do not respond to treatment are probably carriers of the disease and should not be kept in the flock. Following treatment, normal sheep should be placed in an area that has not had sheep on it for two weeks. This will prevent reinfection. Effective antiseptics for the treatment of footrot include:

- 10% zinc sulfate solution (effective and safe, but can be poisonous if consumed by thirsty sheep).

- 10% copper sulfate solution (may be poisonous if the sheep drink the solution).

To prepare a 10% zinc sulfate solution, add 1 kg of zinc sulfate (ZnSO4) to 10 liters of hot water. For a 10% copper sulfate solution, add 1 kg copper sulfate (CuSO4) to 10 liters of hot water. To aid in penetration, add a small amount of detergent to the solution.

Figure 9.19 Hooves should be trimmed to remove rotten tissue.

Note—Formaldehyde is used in some areas as a footbath. However, due to its poisonous properties, formaldehyde should not be used for this purpose.

Overeating Disease (*Clostridium perfringens*)—Sheep affected with this disease are usually found dead with no previous signs of illness. The best growing, healthiest animals are usually affected. The bacteria reside in the intestinal tract and overgrowth occurs when the animal, usually a lamb, is exposed to a large amount of easily digested food. Excessive growth of clostridia is followed by the production of a toxin that poisons the animal. Over consumption of milk, grain or lush grass can result in the condition. Lambs should be vaccinated with clostridium perfringens types C&D at 8 and 12 weeks of age. Ewes should be vaccinated during the last month of pregnancy and will then produce antibodies in the colostrums that will help protect the young lamb.

Tetanus (*Clostridium tetani*)—The tetanus organism is a member of the clostridial family of bacteria. These bacteria live in the soil and invade wounds. Sheep with tetanus are unable to swallow and become completely rigid. Death occurs within several days. Vaccines are available and very effective in prevention of the disease. Tetanus vaccination is sometimes combined with

Figure 9.20 A lamb with tetanus.

the clostridium perfringens vaccines and is given to the ewe during late pregnancy and to the lambs at 8 and 12 weeks of age. Wounds should be cleaned and disinfected and penicillin administered, if possible, to prevent tetanus infection.

Internal Parasites

Roundworms—Sheep are infected with many parasitic worms when they consume the immature or larval stages found in the environment on the forage. The adult worms live in the abomasum (4th stomach) and small intestine and consume blood and protein from the animal. Worm eggs are passed in the manure and contaminate the grazing area. The eggs develop with larvae that hatch on the ground and the larvae then crawl onto the forage, completing the cycle. Animals that have been dewormed will become infected again within three weeks if put back on a contaminated pasture. Larvae may be present for up to a year on a contaminated pasture, especially under warm, moist conditions. Hot, dry conditions will kill the larvae. Lambs are most severely affected by parasites. Older animals develop resistance but serve to contaminate the ground for the lambs. Stomach worms, such as *Haemonchus, Cooperia, Ostertagia,* and others can cause weakness, poor growth, and anemia which can result in bottle jaw. In addition, parasitized lambs have reduced growth efficiency, thus wasting valuable feed resources. Severe cases can result in death.

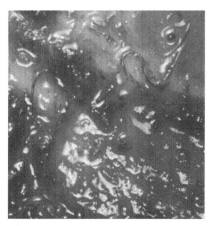

Figure 9.21 Stomach worms (*Haemonchus*).

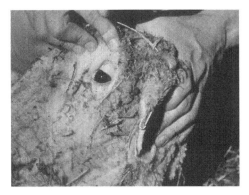

Figure 9.22 Anemia caused by *Haemonchus*.

Figure 9.23 Bottle jaw.

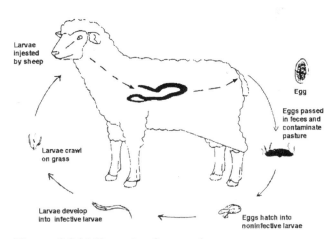

Figure 9.24 Life cycle of stomach worms.

Lungworms—Some lungworms have a similar life cycle to that described for the stomach worms. The sheep consume the larvae while grazing, but unlike stomach worms, these adult parasites develop in the airways of the lungs. Other lungworms require development in an intermediate host before they are infective to the sheep. The adult parasites produce larvae that are coughed up, swallowed and passed in the manure. These larvae then contaminate the grazing area where they are again consumed. As is true for the stomach worms, animals that are treated for parasites and then grazed on a contaminated area rapidly become reinfected. The worms obstruct the airways resulting in difficult breathing, coughing, sneezing and weight loss. Severely affected sheep and goats die from suffocation or secondary bacterial pneumonia. Control involves the use of dewormers that are effective against lungworms (levamisole, fenbendazole, albendazole, and ivermectin) and movement of treated animals to uncontaminated pasture.

Liver Flukes—Liver flukes have an indirect life cycle which requires the presence of a snail as the intermediate host. Thus, the flukes affect sheep that graze wet areas. The banks of irrigation ditches, slow moving streams, ponds and swampy areas are ideal sources for liver flukes. The flukes migrate through the liver causing bleeding and tissue damage. Infected animals become anemic, develop edema and may have liver failure. Death may occur suddenly due to blood loss or after prolonged loss of weight and weakness. Liver flukes cause damage to the liver tissue allowing *Clostridium novyi* to enter and cause Black's disease. Most deworming medications are ineffective against liver flukes. Treatment requires use of specific fluke medications every six months.

Tapeworms—Hydatid disease is caused by *Echinococcus*, a tapeworm of DOGS and other carnivores. Tapeworm segments are passed via the feces and contaminate pastures. Sheep are infected by ingesting either eggs or tapeworm segments. The eggs hatch in the intestine, burrow through the wall and migrate to tissues and develop into large fluid filled cysts called hydatid cysts. These cysts are filled with numerous tapeworm heads (scolices). Each tapeworm head in the cyst can develop into an adult tapeworm when ingested by the canid. These cysts often develop in the liver and lungs and rarely in the brain. **Man can also become infected.** It is extremely important to deworm dogs for tapeworms and not allow dogs to eat any part of a dead sheep that is not cooked. Dogs should be routinely dewormed for the tapeworm, *Echinoccous*. Burn or bury dead sheep to prevent wild carnivores from eating the dead sheep and perpetuating the life cycle of the tapeworm. Other tapeworms can be found in the bile ducts of the liver and in the intestines of sheep. These tapeworms may cause blockages that interfere with digestion or health of the sheep, but also may be present without creating harm to the sheep. They do not infect humans. Dewormers such as fenbendazole and albendazole will kill these parasites.

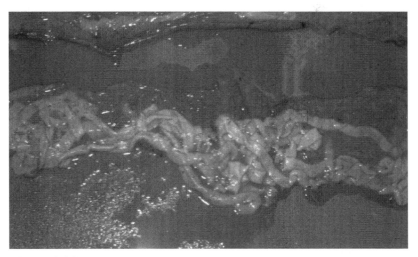

Figure 9.25 Adult tapeworm.

Coccidia—This parasite, unlike those previously described, does not require forage or soil moisture to complete its life cycle. It is a one-celled protozoal parasite that multiplies in the lining of the intestine, causing diarrhea that prevents proper nutrient absorption. Parasite oocysts are passed in the manure, develop and become infective in the environment, and are ingested when the animal consumes manure-contaminated feed or water. Lambs show poor growth rates, thin body condition and diarrhea. Adult animals develop immunity to the coccidian but may shed oocysts, thus contaminating the environment for the young animals. This parasite becomes a problem where animals are kept in covered, confined areas and fed on the ground. Prevention involves the construction of feeders and waterers that prevent manure contamination. Direct sunlight kills the oocysts, but in shaded areas, oocysts can remain infective for more than one year. Lambs and kids that become ill from coccidiosis can be treated with sulfa antibiotics or specific anti-coccidial agents like amprolium. In severely contaminated areas, it may be necessary to include an anti-coccidial agent in the feed (decoquinate, lasalocid).

Figure 9.26 Lambs at feed bunk with coccidia.

Prevention of Internal Parasitism

It is expensive and impractical to completely eliminate parasites from a flock. Instead, control procedures should be instituted that keep parasite levels low. Some general guidelines apply to the control of most internal parasites. These include:

1) Use feeders and waterers that prevent manure contamination when feeding harvested feeds.
2) Construct feeding areas to allow direct sunlight penetration.
3) Deworm the entire flock using the proper dose of a medication effective against the parasites that are present. Hold

sheep off feed overnight before treatment to improve the effectiveness of the medication.

4) Keep animals off the clean pasture for 2 days following treatment for parasites.

5) Following treatment, move the flock to a pasture that is uncontaminated with parasites. Safe pastures include annual forages planted on tilled ground, regrowth of forages following harvesting for hay, and pastures that have not been grazed by sheep or goats for one year.

6) Treat purchased animals for internal parasites before mixing them with the rest of the flock. If possible, check the manure for worm eggs two weeks after deworming to ensure they are not passing worm eggs or only very low numbers.

7) Avoid grazing areas with other flocks that do not follow the above recommendations. An alternate grazing of selected pastures with sheep and cattle will also aid in the control of internal parasites. Cattle can act as a "vacuum cleaner" for many of the sheep worm larvae resulting in a reasonably safe place to go with sheep again after pasture regrowth occurs following cattle grazing. If the climate and soil fertility permit, this can occur multiple times in a single year.

8) Remember that lambs are more susceptible to parasites than adult sheep. If "clean" grazing areas are not available, it may be better to wean the lambs and raise them in dry lots than to pasture them in areas where parasite buildup is a problem.

9) Do not allow dogs, cats or wild carnivores to eat dead sheep or the offal from slaughtered animals. Several parasitic diseases are passed from sheep to carnivores and then back to sheep. Some of these diseases can be transmitted to humans. To break this cycle, it is necessary to prevent carnivores from eating dead sheep. Carcasses and offal, including placentas, should be buried or burned.

Flocks that use controlled breeding and have a specific lambing season should deworm ewes during the last month of pregnancy to decrease the transmission of parasites from the adult animals to the young. Additional treatments may be necessary during the middle of the grazing season and again before the flock is confined for feeding. If an initial treatment is given when animals enter confinement facilities, as occurs during winter feeding, further treatment during confinement should not be necessary.

Haemonchus is one of the main internal parasites of sheep and goats world wide. In areas where there has been overuse of dewormers there is a growing problem with resistant worm populations that threaten production. When dealing with roundworms like *Haemonchus*, depending on your region of the world and the availability of medications, type of forage and grazing system there are some alternative methods which may be used. The basis behind these methods is to reduce parasite burden but limit the parasites' resistance to the medication:

1) Leave 10% of the animals (the biggest and healthiest) untreated.
2) Use a FAMACHA approach where the principle worm problem is *Haemonchus*. This approach will generally leave at least 50% untreated.
3) Treat all the animals and leave them on the pasture for three to five days to pick up a load of unselected worms to take to the clean area.
4) Move the sheep to a safe pasture and wait 3-5 days before deworming to ensure a "refugia" of unselected worms remains to dilute the genes of worms selected by treatment.

When dealing with *Haemonchus* it may be advisable to not treat ewes in the barn. *Haemonchus* does not survive colder winters well on pasture and a similar thing may happen in the tropics during periods of hot days and nights. Treatment of all ewes in confinement prior to going out to pasture will definitely reduce the pasture contamination for their lambs, but it also selects for *Haemonchus* resistance. An alternative is to treat thin ewes, or move the ewes and their lambs to clean areas at least a couple of times before the lambs are weaned to reduce pasture larval buildup.

These concerns are not necessary for tapeworms or coccidia, and lungworms.

Although diagnosis of internal parasitism can often be made on the basis of observation and grazing history, microscopic examination of the feces for eggs and larvae can provide verification and accurate identification of the parasites that inhabit the gastrointestinal tract, the liver and the respiratory tract of sheep. Microscopic examination can give an indication of the severity of parasitism; help determine the most effective worm medication (anthelmintic); and aid in planning a parasite control program. It is important to remember that during the early stages of an infection, ova may not be detected, as during an immature infection, a large number of young, non-egg producing worms may be present.

One of the most common methods of identifying parasite eggs in the feces is the simple flotation technique. A concentrated sugar solution or one of several saturated salt solutions, such as sodium chloride (table salt) or magnesium sulfate (Epsom salt), can be used. The specific gravities of these solutions are higher than the specific gravity of the parasite eggs. Therefore, when fecal material is mixed with one of these saturated solutions, the eggs float to the top.

Method:

1) Mix a small amount (1-2 gm) of fresh fecal material with 20-30 mls of saturated salt solution in a straight-walled glass or plastic cylinder, vial or test tube. The container should be filled until the solution rounds slightly above the top of the tube (forms a convex meniscus).
2) Place a microscope slide on top of the container in contact with the solution. Make sure that no air bubbles are present.
3) Let the mixture stand for 15-20 minutes to allow the eggs to rise to the top.
4) Remove the slide and turn it over. Place a cover slip on the slide.
5) Examine the slide under a microscope using the low power (100X).

Although it does give one an idea of which species of worms are present, the simple float technique is not the most accurate way to diagnose the level of parasitism in sheep. A concentration centrifugation technique that quantitates the number of eggs present per gram of feces gives a much better representation of whole herd health. Fresh fecal samples of 4-8 grams should be submitted to a diagnostic lab where quantitative fecal examinations can be performed.

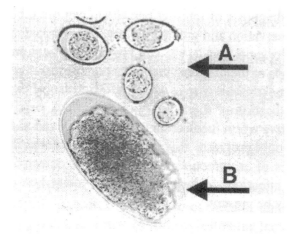

Figure 9.27 A—Coccidian oocysts. B—Stomach worm egg.

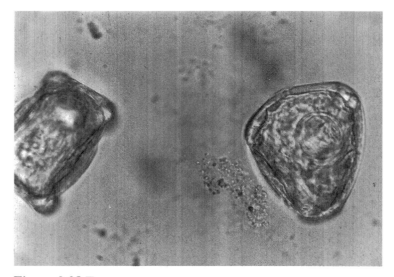

Figure 9.28 Tapeworm eggs.

Diagnosis of some of the internal parasites is based on the presence of larvae in the feces rather than the presence of ova. The Baermann Technique is commonly used to recover larvae from the feces.

Method:

1) Fill a beaker with warm 30-35°C) water.
2) Wrap the fecal sample in gauze or cheese cloth and suspend in a beaker (approximately 500 mls) of water.
3) Leave the feces suspended in the water for 8-12 hours or overnight to allow the larvae to swim out of the fecal material and migrate to the bottom of the beaker.
4) Examine 1-2 drops of the solution from the **very bottom** of the beaker under a microscope at low power (100X). It will be necessary to examine a minimum of 5-10 drops of solution.

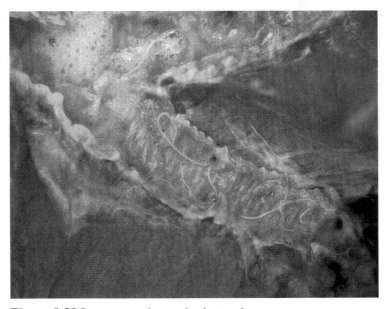

Figure 9.29 Lungworm larvae in the trachea.

External Parasite Control

Like internal parasites, external parasites result in poor quality sheep products and lost income to producers. Common external sheep parasites include lice, keds, mites and ticks. These parasites bite the animal and cause skin irritation, resulting in rubbing, scratching and chewing by sheep. This can lead to damage to the wool and pelt. Some parasites also feed on the sheep's blood. This can cause blood loss anemia, especially in lambs. The result is unthrifty, poorly productive sheep. Blood sucking parasites can also transmit disease.

The best time to treat for external parasites is immediately after shearing. All sheep should be treated with an approved product according to label directions. If infestations are heavy, the treatment should be repeated two weeks later. Pyrethrin-type insecticides, such as Ectrin, Expar and Elector, are safe and effective and can be used on pregnant ewes. They are applied in a liquid form in a line down the animals back. In some countries, the sheep are immersed in a vat or trough containing insecticides (called dipping). Some of these insecticides can be very poisonous and care should be taken to avoid contact with the shepherd's skin. High power sprayers or dusters are also sometimes used to treat animals for external parasites.

Figure 9.30 External parasites (scabies).

Section 10

Shelter, Fencing and Protection from Predators

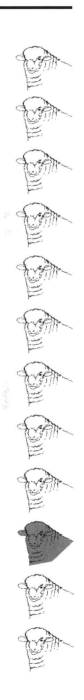

SHELTER, FENCING AND PROTECTION FROM PREDATORS

Shelter

Because of their hardy nature, sheep require relatively little shelter. Indeed, they are very susceptible to pneumonia if kept indoors, and under most circumstances should be kept outside. In desert climates, they will benefit from some shade during the hottest part of the day. A roof of woven branches or cloth with open sides works well (figure 10.1). Good circulation of air is important to prevent overheating.

Figure 10.1 A shaded area provides relief from the hot sun.

In regions that experience freezing rain, snowstorms or sandstorms, the sheep should be provided with a windbreak. This may be a shrub or tree line, a fence, or the side of a building. Newborn lambs cannot regulate their body temperature well and require protection from bold, wet and windy conditions. Ewes that are about to lamb or have just given birth should be placed in a clean sheltered spot until the lambs are dry and have nursed.

Figure 10.2 Lambing pens provide protection from cold, wet and windy conditions.

Fencing

In some parts of the world sheep are grazed over large areas of communal land with a herder in attendance. In this type of system, fencing is usually not used. In other regions, the sheep are completely confined, either in pens, in building or tethered. Many producers use a combination of these systems. Options are available for fencing materials depending on the resources available. They include woven branches, cement or adobe blocks or bricks, rope netting, woven wire and electric wire. Again, the cost of materials must be kept in mind as well as the needs of the shepherd. In some cases, portability may be necessary where in others the structure is permanent. Electric fences can be run off of solar charged batteries and may be useful in areas where confinement of the sheep during grazing and protection from predators is necessary. This type of fencing is expensive, however, and where labor costs are low it may be more economical to use herders.

Figure 10.3 Portable fences help manage grazing and control predators.

Figure 10.4 Electric fences work well with rotational grazing systems.

Protection from Predators

Sheep have no natural defenses and are easy targets for predators. Wolves, bears, coyotes and dogs can all kill adult sheep. Smaller predators like foxes and birds of prey will kill lambs. Theft from human predators is a problem in some places. Guard animals have been used to protect sheep in many parts of the world. Large dogs of breeds that bond to the flock and protect them are very effective (figure 10.5). In addition, donkeys, llamas and cattle will sometimes protect sheep that graze with them (figures 10.6 and 10.7). In some regions, herders stay with the flock at all times to keep them from harm. Flocks are often confined in a predator-proof area near the home at night to avoid losses.

Figure 10.5 Pyrenees guard dog.

Figure 10.6 Guard llama with a large flock of ewes.

Figure 10.7 Guard donkey with ewes.

Section 11

Sanitation, Product Quality and Safety

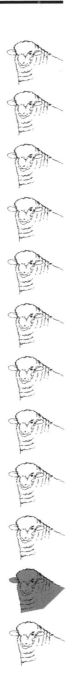

SANITATION, PRODUCT QUALITY AND SAFETY

Sanitation

Proper sanitation is important for several reasons. First, it reduces disease. Fewer disease problems result in lower production costs. Second, since healthy sheep require fewer drugs, the risk of residues occurring in meat and milk are reduced. Third, proper sanitation reduces the likelihood of bacterial contamination of meat and milk products. Food poisoning from bacteria such as *E. coli* and *Salmonella* cause significant illness, and sometimes death, in humans. Fourth, bacteria in meat or milk products cause rapid spoiling. These organisms are frequently found in the feces of livestock. Milk from dairy sheep can pick up unacceptable odors and flavors from being exposed to a dirty environment. For these reasons, it is very important that every measure be taken to keep livestock facilities clean.

Sanitation includes both cleaning and disinfection. The most important aspect of sanitation in livestock facilities is the removal of manure. Regular removal of manure prevents the buildup of bacteria and parasites in the environment.

Wet conditions also contribute to poor sanitation and disease problems. Bacteria grow rapidly in standing water and mud. When sheep are confined, it is important to provide dry areas for bedding down. This can be accomplished by providing good drainage or by creating a raised mound. Feeding and watering areas should also be well-drained.

The accumulation of dirt, mud, and manure on the fleece can result in contamination of the carcass at slaughter during pelt removal (figure 11.1). Bacteria transferred from the pelt to the carcass can contaminate the meat. Soiled fleeces on dairy sheep can contaminate milk at milking time.

Disinfection involves the use of chemicals to kill disease-causing organisms on equipment or facilities. Commercial disinfectants or a dilute sodium hypochlorite solution (15 ml/liter or 2 oz/gal water) can be used. Disinfectants are inactivated by manure and other organic materials. Therefore, it is important to do a thorough job of cleaning before using a disinfectant. Always follow label directions for exposure time and rinsing instructions when using disinfectants.

Sheep are often exposed to contagious diseases when their feed or water is contaminated with manure, urine, nasal secretions, or uterine discharges. Keep sick animals separated to help prevent the contamination of feed and water supplies. Feeders and waterers should be cleaned and disinfected regularly to prevent the buildup of disease-causing agents. Exposure of feeders, waterers and bedding areas to direct sunlight will also help to control infectious agents.

Figure 11.1 Wet, dirty conditions can result in carcass contamination at slaughter.

Product Quality and Safety

Remember that any substance administered to food-producing animals can contaminate food products. Medications, such as antibiotics, dewormers and vaccines, require a withholding period before the meat or milk can safely be consumed. Read the label of all products and carefully follow withdrawal times. Likewise, to prevent food poisoning, good hygiene must be practiced during the milking and slaughter procedures. Meat and milk must be kept in cold storage to prevent the growth of bacteria. Meat should always be thoroughly cooked and never consumed raw. Milk should be pasteurized before drinking, and cheeses made from unpasteurized milk should be well-aged or soaked in salt brine to kill any bacteria present.

Figure 11.2 Product quality and safety are important to human health.

Section 12

Cooperative and Conservation Programs

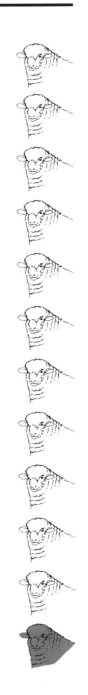

COOPERATIVE AND CONSERVATION PROGRAMS

Marketing Cooperatives

Many small flock holders have excess lamb or wool that can be marketed. The income from these products can be used for family needs. Marketing in small quantities often results in low prices for the product. To receive the most from sales, a community may benefit from organizing a marketing cooperative. A group of producers from the community can call together a meeting to outline the goals and structure of their marketing organization. The advantage of a marketing cooperative is that the products from a number of producers can be pooled and presented for bids to a number of potential buyers. To attract competitive bids, the producers must have a uniform, high-quality product. This can be achieved if the members of the cooperative set their own product standards and all members meet those standards. The members

Figure 12.1 Marketing cooperative producers weighing lambs before sale.

will want to review these standards on a periodic basis. They may need to be adjusted as markets change.

Genetic Improvement Cooperatives

To provide a high quality, uniform product the cooperative may assist producers with genetic improvement. Some small flock owners cannot afford the expense of a good quality male. Often they use males that are closely related to their ewes, resulting in poor quality offspring. The use of unrelated males with superior characteristics will improve the health and production of the flock. Again, the producers must outline the goals they want to achieve. They can then develop minimum standards for the male. This male of superior genetics can be used to improve the quality of their individual flocks. A good healthy male given good care and nutrition can serve 100 ewes. It may be necessary for a number of producers to pool their ewes during the breeding season. The breeding season could be for 21 days, after which the ewes could go back to their homes. Well-nourished ewes will usually conceive during this short period. A less expensive male could be used after this 21 day period to breed those that did not conceive earlier.

Figure 12.2 A male with superior genetics should be used to improve the quality of the flock.

Conservation Programs

Sheep can fit into a variety of conservation programs. In many areas, cultivation or overgrazing has exposed the top soil to wind and/or water erosion leaving the area unproductive. In areas too steep for cultivation, trees, shrubs or other soil binding plants can be established. Certain grasses can also be established to prevent erosion. Some of these plants improve the soil by producing nitrogen and adding organic matter. If the slope is too steep and the soil is susceptible to erosion, trees, shrubs, grasses and other plants should be established to stabilize the soil. These plants are an excellent source of high quality feed that can be harvested on a daily basis and fed to sheep. In forested areas, sheep can be utilized to control plant undergrowth that is harmful to forest timber production and that may increase the fire danger. Managed correctly, sheep can be used in many ecosystems increasing the productivity of the land while producing milk, meat and fiber for the family.

Figure 12.3 Sheep can add to the productivity of many ecosystems.

Appendix

SELECTIVE WEIGHTS AND MEASURES, EQUIVALENTS AND CONVERSIONS

Volume:
1 teaspoon = 5 cubic centimeters (cc) = 5 milliliters (ml)
3 teaspoons = 1 tablespoon
1 tablespoon = 15 cc = 15 ml
2 tablespoons = one fluid ounce
8 ounces = 1 cup = 240 ml
2 cups = 1 pint = 480 ml
2 pints = 1 quart
4 quarts = 1 gallon
1 quart = approximately 1 liter (1)

Weight:
16 ounces = 1 pound (lb)
1 pound = 454 grams (gm)
2.2 pounds = 1 kilogram (kg)
1 ounce = 28 grams

Metric:
1 milliliter (ml) = 1 cubic centimeter (cc)
1000 ml = 1 liter
1000 milligrams (mg) = 1 gram
1000 g = 1 kilogram (kg)

Conversion Factors:
Temperature Conversion
   Celsius ° = 5/9 (F° - 32°)
   Fahrenheit ° = 9/5 (C° + 32°)

To convert percent to ppm, move the decimal point 4 places to the right.
For example, 0.01% = 100 ppm.

THE END

Made in the USA
Lexington, KY
08 September 2014